DELICIOUS RECIPES FOR A HEALTHIER, HAPPIER LIFE

WW Healthy You

The small print

EGGS We use medium eggs, unless otherwise stated. Pregnant women, the elderly and children should avoid recipes with eggs which are raw or not fully cooked.

FRUIT AND VEGETABLES Recipes use medium-size fruit and veg, unless otherwise stated.

REDUCED-FAT SOFT CHEESE Where a recipe uses reduced-fat soft cheese, we mean a soft cheese with 30% less fat than its full-fat equivalent.

LOW-FAT SPREAD When a recipe uses a low-fat spread, we mean a spread with a fat content of no more than 39%.

MICROWAVES If we have used a microwave in any of our recipes, the timings will be for an 850-watt microwave oven.

PREP AND COOK TIMES These are approximate and meant to be guidelines only. The prep time includes all the steps up to and following the main cooking time(s). The stated cook times may vary according to your oven.

GLUTEN FREE
Recipes labelled as gluten free, or displaying the gluten free icon, only include ingredients that naturally do not contain gluten. Whenever using tinned, bottled or other types of packaged processed ingredients, such as sauces and stocks, it is essential to check that those ingredients do not contain gluten. Gluten-containing ingredients such as wheat, barley and rye will be highlighted in bold on the product's label. Manufacturers may also indicate whether there is a chance that their product may have been accidentally contaminated with gluten during the manufacturing process.

SMARTPOINTS have been calculated using the values for generic foods, not brands (except where stated). Tracking using branded items may affect the recorded SmartPoints.

WHEN YOU SEE THESE SYMBOLS:

Tells you how many SmartPoints are in the recipe.

 Indicates a recipe is suitable for freezing.

 Indicates a No Count recipe.

GF Indicates a recipe is gluten free or can be made gluten free with a few simple swaps, for example by using gluten free soy sauce.

V Indicates a recipe is vegetarian.

Seven.

Produced by Seven Publishing on behalf of Weight Watchers International, Inc. Published January 2017.

First published in Great Britain by Seven Publishing Ltd.

Seven Publishing Ltd
3-7 Herbal Hill
London
EC1R 5EJ
www.seven.co.uk

10 9 8 7 6 5 4 3 2 1

A CIP catalogue record for this book is available from the British Library.
ISBN: 978-0-9935835-4-4

WEIGHT WATCHERS PUBLICATIONS TEAM
Imogen Prescott, Samantha Rees, Nicola Kirk, Stephanie Williams, Ruby Bamford

FOR SEVEN PUBLISHING LTD
FOOD
Food editor Sarah Akhurst
Food assistants Linzi Brechin, Nadine Brown, Gabriella English

EDITORIAL
Editor-in-Chief Helen Renshaw
Editor Ward Hellewell **Sub-editors** Clare Devane, Oliver Fritz

DESIGN & PHOTOGRAPHY
Art director Liz Baird
Photography Alex Luck **Food team photography** Lydia Evans
Food stylist Sarah Cook, assisted by Lydia McKee
Prop stylist Luis Peral
Picture editor Carl Palmer
Hair and make-up Jolanda Coetzer, assisted by Jenni Davies
Thanks to Studio RW for the hand-thrown ceramics

ACCOUNT MANAGEMENT
Account manager Jo Brennan
Business director, retail Andy Roughton
Group publishing director Kirsten Price

PRODUCTION
Production director Sophie Dillon
Colour reproduction by F1 Colour **Printed in Italy** by Rotolito Lombarda.

Contents

Welcome to the Healthy You cookbook

At Weight Watchers we love food. Delicious and healthy food is at the heart of our plan and at the heart of this book. In **Healthy You**, you'll find not only a collection of tasty recipes but also weekly meal plans to help you fit healthy eating into your life.

We've got **meal plans** for one, two, and the whole family. We've also got plans for when you've got a busy week, for when meat isn't on the menu, or for when you're on No Count.

We all know that **planning ahead** helps you to **stay on track**. It also means less time staring aimlessly into the fridge, shopping becomes quicker and there's less waste, so your wallet will benefit too.

With **loads of ideas** for breakfast, lunch and dinner, as well as snacks and puds, you'll have **all the inspiration** you need to feel in control and to eat well.

The WW Kitchen Team

Healthy eating

with the WW Kitchen Team

All about this book

Meet the WW Kitchen Team – they're here to help you find food inspiration and show you how easy it is to plan your weekly meals.

The WW Kitchen Team – Nadine, Linzi and Sarah, the team behind the Weight Watchers recipes, have captured some of their favourite meals and most valuable meal planning tips and advice in this book. Whether you're counting or not, you'll find amazing food, ideas and ready-made plans (see page 210) to suit you.

Why plan?

Meal planning is an important part of healthy eating. By planning ahead you take the guesswork out of what you're eating, and can feel confident knowing you're on the path to a healthy you. Getting organised and thinking about the week ahead is a great way to stay positive, focused and motivated. For some handy meal planning tips and smart shopping advice, see page 24.

> ‘Getting organised and thinking about your week ahead is also a great way to stay *positive, focused* and *motivated*’

When you're counting SmartPoints

You can either create your own meal plan or use one of our ready-made plans for inspiration. We've given you breakfast, lunch and dinner ideas, and you can use the remainder of your SmartPoints allowance on snacks, puds and drinks. You'll also get your weekly allowance to use however you like. Most fruits and vegetables are zero SmartPoints, so use them to your advantage – they're especially good as between-meal snacks, and fresh fruit is also great for desserts. If your chosen meals for the day takes you over your daily allowance then you can dip into your weekly SmartPoints allowance to make up the difference.

When you're following No Count

All you have to do is stick to the list of No Count foods and flavour boosters and you know you're on the right track. There's no measuring, no weighing and no tracking. You just eat until you feel satisfied. To create your own No Count meal plan, choose recipes that only use ingredients from the No Count food list – they will be marked with the green No Count symbol (see page 6). Some of the recipes in this book can be adapted to make them No Count – you'll find cook's tips that will explain how to do this. You get a daily allowance of 2 teaspoons of healthy oils each day that you can use in recipes or dressings. You'll also get a weekly allowance for foods that are not on the list, so you can still enjoy any foods or drinks you may miss. For the full No Count food list, see page 222, and for some quick and simple ideas for No Count meals, turn to page 16.

The SmartPoints way

If you're counting, here's a quick guide to how it works, and how to build your meal plans around it.

What are SmartPoints?

Every food has a SmartPoints value – one easy-to-use number that's based on four components: calories, protein, sugar and saturated fat. The idea is to steer you towards nutritious, healthier foods, so even if two foods have the same calories, it doesn't mean they'll have the same SmartPoints; foods that are higher in sugar and saturated fat will have more SmartPoints.

How do I know how many SmartPoints a food has?

All of the recipes in this book have SmartPoints included, both for the whole recipe and for each individual serving. To find out the SmartPoints for individual ingredients, branded foods, drinks and even restaurant meals that you may want to include in your meal plans, you can go online and access the SmartPoints calculator or use the app (subscribers only). You can also pick up copies of *Eat Out* and *Shop* in your meeting, or buy them online.

How many SmartPoints do I get each day?

Your SmartPoints budget is personal to you and will be given to you when you join Weight Watchers. Unused SmartPoints from your daily allowance can't be carried over to the next day, so use them or lose them!

What can I use weekly SmartPoints for?

As well as your daily SmartPoints, you also get weekly SmartPoints to play with. You can use these any way you like. Split them up over the week, save them all for the weekend or don't use them at all. The choice is yours.

> ‘As long as you stick to your SmartPoints budget, you can plan your meals however you like’

How do I create a SmartPoints meal plan?

In this book, you'll find dozens of delicious recipes for breakfasts, lunches and dinners, as well as snacks and puds, and it's easy to create meal plans that include all of these elements each day. As long as you stick to your SmartPoints budget, you can plan your meals however you like. For example, you may want your main meal to be at lunch time, or you may want to skip the dessert and have an extra morning or afternoon snack instead. It's up to you how you allocate your SmartPoints throughout the day. Get started with our ready-made meal plans on page 210 – they add up to no more than 26 SmartPoints.

WEIGHING AND MEASURING

Because the SmartPoints value of every food is based on its portion size, it's a good idea to get into the habit of weighing and measuring everything you're eating. It won't take long for you to get to the stage where you're able to judge portion sizes by eye, but until then, you'll find a set of kitchen scales and measuring spoons useful kitchen additions.

cmx.weightwatchers.co.uk
Weight Watchers Tracker
Favourites
My Food
Weight
Food Log
18
SmartPoints left
28 Weekly SmartPoints™ & 0 FitPoints™ left
+Track Breakfast
+Track Lunch
+Track Dinner
+Track Snacks
1 serving(s)
BREAKFAST
Overnight oats with apricots
LUNCH
DINNER
SNACKS
Latte
Apple(s)
1 medium
SEE ALL
LATEST RECIPES

NO COUNT know-how

The No Count food list on page 222 is full of foods you can turn into quick, tasty meals to include in your meal plans. Here are five of the most versatile ingredients, and some fast, fabulous ways to use them.

1 POTATOES
Jackets and wedges

Jacket potatoes and wedges are a great lunch or dinner option when served with a No Count topping such as baked beans, tinned tuna, cottage cheese or chilli con carne (see p166). For wedges, see the recipe on page 126. For jackets, prick the skin with a fork, put them directly onto the oven shelf and bake at 200°C, fan 180°, gas mark 6 for about 1 hour.

Fish cakes

Add tinned tuna or salmon and chopped onion and parsley to plain mashed potato. Form into cakes, then dip in beaten egg and roll in breadcrumbs made from Weight Watchers Brown Bread. Mist with cooking spray, then put on a baking tray and cook in the oven at 200°C, fan 180°C, gas mark 6 for 15 minutes, turning once.

2 WHOLEWHEAT PASTA
Spaghetti carbonara

Whisk together an egg with 1 tablespoon 0% fat Greek yogurt and season. Saute chopped bacon and sliced button mushrooms in a nonstick pan misted with cooking spray. Cook and drain wholewheat pasta, then return it to the pan, add the ham and mushrooms and stir in the egg and yogurt. The heat of the pasta will cook the sauce.

Pasta salad

Mix cooked wholewheat pasta shapes with chopped lean ham and chopped veg – try celery, onion, red pepper, sweetcorn and cucumber, then add some 0% fat Greek yogurt, a squeeze of lemon juice, some chopped fresh parsley and seasoning.

3 EGGS
Omelette

The perfect No Count fast food – super simple and ready in a flash. To serve 1, beat two eggs and season. Heat a small nonstick frying pan over a medium-high heat and mist with calorie controlled cooking spray. Pour in the eggs and swirl to coat the base, then cook until almost set. Top with your chosen No Count filling – try cooked asparagus and low-fat cottage cheese.

Chicken & sweetcorn soup

Enrich a soup with a beaten egg. For a Chinese restaurant favourite, start with chicken stock made from a stock cube, add chopped cooked chicken and sweetcorn that's been roughly puréed in a food processor. Bring to a simmer, then drizzle in a beaten egg and serve with chopped spring onions.

4 TINNED FRUIT
Fruit fool

Purée drained tinned fruit (in fruit juice) – try peaches, apricots or mangoes – then swirl it through Quark, spoon into glasses and chill.

Ice lollies

Drain and purée tinned fruits (in fruit juice) – try pears, cherries peaches or mangoes, and mix with unsweetened almond or soya milk and freeze in ice lolly moulds. Add other flavours that take your fancy – fresh mint, grated ginger or vanilla.

5 WEIGHT WATCHERS PITTAS
Pitta pizza

Spread pitta breads with passata, sprinkle on dried herbs, then add No Count toppings – try prawns, tomatoes, peppers, onions or mushrooms, but don't overload the pizza. Dot over cottage cheese, then season and bake at 200°C, fan 180°C, gas mark 6 for 10 minutes.

Kebabs

Marinate chunks of skinless chicken breast fillet in low-fat natural yogurt and spices, then put on skewers and grill. Warm pittas, then fill them with the chicken, shredded lettuce, red onions, tomatoes and cucumber, and top with 0% fat natural Greek yogurt, dried chilli or hot pepper sauce.

Make a meal plan

Time spent meal planning is time well spent. If you've never done it before, here's a step-by-step guide to do it the easy way.

1 START by flicking through our delicious recipes. We've made it easy by dividing the sections into breakfast, lunch, dinner and snacks and puds. Make a note of the recipes that appeal to you and just follow your instincts – you know what you like best.

2 ADD YOUR OWN IDEAS As well as the recipes in this book, you can include your own favourite meal ideas. Think about what you'll be doing during the week – on a busy day, you might want a quick and simple standby, like an omelette or salad.

3 CHECK YOUR CUPBOARDS
Take a quick look inside your fridge and storecupboard to see what ingredients you have on hand. This may help you to come up with ideas and ways to use things you've already got. See p20 for a list of cooking essentials.

COOKING AHEAD means you'll need to make space in your freezer. Clear out unwanted food, then make sure you label and date foods as you put them in, so there's no confusion.

4 WRITE IT ALL DOWN Take a sheet of paper and make seven rows for the days and then columns for breakfast, lunch and dinner, then fill in the blanks. Include the SmartPoints values if you're counting and add them up to ensure you don't exceed your allowance.

5 ADD EXTRAS Don't forget to add a few snacks to your meal plans. Focus on including those lovely zero heroes – lots of healthy fruit and vegetables. They make the perfect take-anywhere, ready-to-eat snacks.

PREPPING AHEAD is a great way to save time in the kitchen later. If possible, do it straight after shopping. Why not divide meat into separate portions before freezing, and chop veg then put them in zip-lock bags and keep them in the fridge or freezer for later.

FLAVOUR PACKED Keep your meals interesting and tasty – buy potted herbs and keep them watered and on the windowsill so you can just snip and cook. Also keep fresh garlic, chilli, ginger, limes and other favourites to hand.

6 STREAMLINE Once you've filled in all the meals for the week, review your plan to see how it's working. Will you really have time to make a different meal every night? Or could you make life easier by batch cooking (see below) and using what you've made for two or more meals in the same week?

DOUBLE UP Cook once, eat twice. It's a no-brainer to batch cook, especially if you're making something like a soup, stew or ragù sauce for pasta (see p164). Not only will it save you time, it also helps you avoid waste and save money. Double up on other elements like cooked veg and grains, too. Freeze food in individual portions in freezer bags – all you need to do is reheat.

7 MAKE A SHOPPING LIST **Write down all the ingredients and the quantities you'll need for your meals – that way you'll shop purposefully, and there'll be less chance of making impulse purchases, or buying things you don't need, meaning you'll avoid waste. Again, check your cupboards and fridge to see what ingredients you already have.**

NEED IDEAS? If you find yourself stuck for ideas, keep a meal journal – it's a good way to remember recipes and snacks that you love, so you can use them in future meal plans. It's also a great way to stay motivated, as you keep track of how you feel as you lose weight.

8 STICK TO IT Now you're ready to turn your plan into action. It's not always easy, but if you stick to your meal plans as closely as you can, you'll soon be reaping the rewards. Good luck!

DRINK SMART Many drinks have SmartPoints so you will need to think about these as you're creating your meal plan. See p22 for some ideas.

TAKE STOCK

Storecupboard essentials

You've made your shopping list, now check your storecupboard to see what you've got on hand.

Keeping your cupboard stocked is an important part of getting organised in the kitchen. Knowing you've got all those essential dry and tinned ingredients means you'll be able to make lots of healthy meals, even at a moment's notice. Here are some storecupboard staples that will cover all of the recipes in this book – add any others that you regularly use to the list.

COOKING BASICS

Calorie controlled cooking spray
Honey
Lemon juice
Olive oil
Stock cubes (gluten free)
Tomato paste
Vinegar

PASTA, GRAINS & PULSES

Chickpeas (tinned)
Couscous
Flour
Kidney beans (tinned)
Lentils
Microwaveable rice
Noodles (dried and wok-ready)
Pasta (wholemeal)
Quinoa
Porridge oats (gluten free)
Rice (brown)

FLAVOURINGS & SAUCES

Chilli flakes (dried)
Chilli sauce
Fish sauce
Harissa paste
Herbs (dried)
Peanut butter (reduced-fat)
Soy sauce (gluten free)
Spices and seasonings
Coconut milk (reduced-fat)

TINS & JARS

Baked beans (reduced sugar and salt)
Capers
Olives
Passata
Salmon
Sweetcorn
Tomatoes (chopped)
Tuna

- **Ensure products are gluten free if you need to.**

'I have a good clear out of my storecupboard every six months or so. My top tip? Put dried goods like oats and pasta into airtight clear containers. That way, they'll keep for longer, and you can see at a glance exactly what you've got.' *Linzi*

Organico
CHOPPED TOMATO
From Tuscany
KIKKOMA
150ml
LEA & PERRINS
WORCESTERSHIRE SAUCE
TABASCO
BRAND
BALSAMIC
VINEGAR
OF MODENA
FLAVO{U}R 21
BOMBA!
The only
1 Cal
spray
Fry light
1CAL
Sunflower Oi
COOKING SPRAY
Noodles
cooks&co
ROASTED
RED PEPPERS
SAITAKU
RICE
VINEGAR
FOR SUSHI
Colman's
Mustard
57g
La Chinata
Pasta
Tilda
The only
1 Cal
spray
Fry light
1CAL
Olive Oil

The WW kitchen team's top 5 drinks

Drinking the wrong things can add SmartPoints without you even realising it, so keep this in mind when creating your meal plans. Forget milky coffees and sugar-laden juices – try these equally delicious, but healthier alternatives.

INFUSED WATER
Crush fresh fruit and herbs in a glass then top up with ice and water (use sparkling if you like). Try peaches, melon, cucumber or berries with mint, lemon verbena, ginger or orange or lemon zest. Zero SmartPoints.

COCONUT WATER
Unflavoured and unsweetened coconut water is refreshing and delicious. Great on its own, or try whizzing it with some watermelon chunks, a splash of lemon juice and some fresh mint. It's 3 SmartPoints per 250ml serving.

ALTERNATIVE MILK
For a warm or cold drink, try unsweetened plant-based milks. Soya milk is 2 SmartPoints per 250ml, while almond milk is 1 SmartPoint per 250ml – both are No Count. Add flavour with vanilla or cinnamon.

TEA
Black, green or fruit teas can be drunk hot or cold – add a slice of lemon, orange or lime for extra flavour. You could also try making an extra-strong brew and topping it up with fizzy water for a fruit tea soda. Zero SmartPoints.

TOMATO JUICE
Make your own vegetable drink using a juicer or blender. Try peppers, tomatoes and celery; add citrus juice to bring out the flavours, and a pinch of cayenne pepper to spice it up. 3 SmartPoints per 250ml.

Smart shopping

Making a list is a great way to stay on track in the supermarket. Here are some other top tips for shopping the smart way.

SNACK FIRST

Shopping when you're hungry is not a great idea. Have an apple before you go – research shows that eating a small, healthy snack before shopping means you're more likely to return home with healthier food.

SORT YOUR LIST

To make your shopping trip more efficient, organise your shopping list in the order that you'll find things in the store.

TAKE YOUR TIME

If you're doing a big shop, give yourself ample time to make the right choices to support a healthy lifestyle. Once it becomes a habit, you'll know exactly what to reach for and what to avoid.

DON'T GO THERE!

Put your blinkers on and move swiftly past the junk food, bakery, sweets and alcohol aisles. Not only will it help you avoid impulse buys, it'll also make your shopping trip shorter. So exert your willpower and feel virtuous afterwards.

ONLINE EASY

If you're time poor, shop online. That way, you can shop anytime and arrange for delivery at your convenience. You're more likely to stick to your shopping list, and you don't need to take the kids!

EMBRACE THE ROUTINE

Try to shop at the same time each week – making grocery shopping part of your regular routine makes it less stressful, helping you to make better choices.

SHOP MINDFULLY

Clever lighting, strategically placed items, the smell of freshly baked bread – supermarkets have lots of tricks to get you to buy. Next time you're tempted to pick up an item that's not on your list, stop and ask yourself if you really need it. We make many of our food choices unconsciously, so being more mindful when shopping will help ensure you're choosing healthier foods.

SMALL IS BETTER

Downsize your trolley to a smaller one or even a basket. You'll be less inclined to fill it with extra items.

READ THE LABEL

Check the labels on tinned foods and packets and look for healthier options that are lower in salt, fat and sugar. Less is more when it comes to those added ingredients. Trans-fats, hydrogenated oils, artificial colours? Just say no!

DEAL OR NO DEAL

We're all guilty of over-buying because of the deals and special offers in supermarkets. But massive bags of spuds or veg can sometimes lead to more food waste, so it more often than not turns out to be a false economy.

A guide to seasonal foods

You've probably heard about how we should all be buying and eating fresh fruit and vegetables when they're in season, but these days, most of them are available all year round, so why does it matter?

For starters, seeking out foods when they're in season will make you think more carefully about what you're eating and encourage you to try a wider variety of foods. Chances are, non-seasonal fruit and vegetables have had to be flown in (often from the other side of the world, so there's also an impact on the environment) or they may have been harvested much earlier and kept in cold storage. The longer something takes to reach your table from the time it was harvested, the more nutrients are lost, and the flavour of the food may also have suffered. On top of that, food flown in from afar, or grown out-of-season in greenhouses will most likely cost you more.

Of course, not all fruit and vegetables are grown in the UK, and that shouldn't mean you can't eat them. As a rule, the closer to home it's grown, the fresher it's likely to be. Keep your eye on prices – when things become cheaper, they're generally in season. Eating home-grown produce is also a great way to support our local farmers and fishers, so if you've got a farmer's market nearby, pay it a visit! Here's a guide to home-grown fruit and veg and when they're in season...

Spring

VEGETABLES
• Asparagus • Carrots • Cauliflower • Celeriac • Cucumber • Curly Kale • Purple Sprouting Broccoli • Savoy Cabbage • Sorrel • Spinach • Spring Greens • Spring Onion • Watercress

FRUIT
• Gooseberries • Rhubarb

Summer

VEGETABLES
• Beetroot • Broad Beans • Carrots • Cauliflower • Courgettes • Cucumber • Fennel • Fresh Peas • Garlic • Green Beans • Lettuce & Salad Leaves • New potatoes • Radishes • Runner Beans • Sage • Salad Onions • Squash • Tomatoes • Watercress

FRUIT
• Blueberries • Cherries • Currants • Greengages • Loganberries • Plums • Raspberries • Strawberries

Autumn

VEGETABLES
• Field Mushrooms • Lettuce • Marrow • Potatoes • Pumpkin • Rocket • Squashes • Sweetcorn • Watercress

FRUIT:
• Apples • Blackberries • Damsons • Elderberries • Pears • Plums • Sloes

Winter

VEGETABLES:
• Bay Leaves • Brussels Sprouts • Cabbage • Carrots • Cauliflower • Celeriac • Curly Kale • Fennel • Leeks • Parsnips • Potatoes • Red Cabbage • Swede • Turnips

FRUIT:
• Apples • Forced Rhubarb • Pears • Quince

Breakfast

All-day breakfast

The good things in life don't have to be off-limits. When you fancy an extra-special breakfast treat, enjoy this classic fry-up.

Serves 4 **Prep time** 6 minutes **Cook time** 25 minutes

Calorie controlled cooking spray
4 reduced-fat pork sausages
300g mushrooms, sliced
150ml vegetable stock, made with ½ cube
420g tin reduced-sugar-and-salt baked beans
4 rashers Weight Watchers Extra Trimmed Unsmoked Back Bacon
4 tomatoes, halved
4 eggs
4 slices Weight Watchers Soft White Danish bread
4 teaspoons low-fat spread

1 Preheat the grill to medium. Mist a large nonstick frying pan with the cooking spray. Put the sausages in the pan and cook over a medium heat for 15 minutes, according to pack instructions.

2 Meanwhile, put the mushrooms and stock into a large pan. Bring to the boil, then simmer for 5-6 minutes, stirring occasionally. Put the beans into a separate pan and heat gently, stirring occasionally.

3 Arrange the bacon rashers on the grill rack with the tomatoes. Cook for 4-5 minutes, turning the rashers once, until crispy.

4 When the sausages are cooked, keep them on a warm plate. Break the eggs into the pan and cook over a medium heat for 2-3 minutes. Toast the bread and spread with low-fat spread.

5 Divide the sausages, mushrooms, beans, bacon and tomatoes between 4 warmed plates. Meanwhile, put the eggs under the grill for a few moments to set the tops. Serve seasoned with black pepper, with the toast on the side.

SmartPoints values per serving 9
SmartPoints values per recipe 34

Granola & Greek yogurt pots with maple raspberries

Crunchy granola and creamy yogurt is perfectly balanced with zingy raspberries and maple syrup.

Serves 6 **Prep time** 10 minutes plus cooling **Cook time** 15-20 minutes

1 tablespoon groundnut oil
2 tablespoons maple syrup
150g rolled oats (ensure gluten free)
1 tablespoon desiccated coconut
Finely grated zest of 1 orange

FOR THE RASPBERRIES
300g raspberries
3 teaspoons maple syrup
6 tablespoons 0% fat natural Greek yogurt

1 Preheat the oven to 150°C, fan 130°C, gas mark 2. Combine the oil and maple syrup in a small pan and warm through.

2 Mix together the oats, coconut and orange zest in a large bowl and stir in the oil mixture until well-coated. Scatter the mixture over a shallow baking tray and bake for 10-15 minutes or until golden, occasionally shaking gently. Remove from the oven and leave to cool on the tray until the granola is completely cold.

3 Meanwhile, gently heat the raspberries with the maple syrup in a small pan until they start to release their juice. Cool slightly, then divide between 6 individual jars or bowls. Top each one with 1 tablespoon of the yogurt and 25g of the granola.

SmartPoints values per serving 6
SmartPoints values per recipe 35

COOK'S TIP

After scattering the granola on the tray, press down with a spatula to make a uniform layer so it cooks evenly.

The turkey, egg & avocado big breakfast

Get set for the day ahead with this flavoursome breakfast of turkey, poached eggs and avocado on toast – what's not to like?

Serves 2 **Prep time** 5 minutes **Cook time** 6 minutes

2 x 25g slices granary original small sliced bread (or any bread that's 2 SmartPoints per slice)
¼ avocado, peeled and stone removed
2 slices tomato
2 slices wafer-thin turkey
A few fresh basil leaves
2 eggs
Small handful of rocket leaves

1 Toast the bread.

2 Mash the avocado in a bowl and spread it over the toast. Add the tomato, turkey and basil to each piece of toast.

3 Poach the eggs in a pan of boiling water (around 3 minutes for a soft yolk and 4 minutes for a firmer one).

4 When the eggs are cooked to your liking, drain and put an egg on top of each piece of turkey. Season with freshly ground black pepper and serve one slice per person with the rocket on the side.

SmartPoints values per serving 6
SmartPoints values per recipe 12

Plum compote with cinnamon & orange

Lightly spiced poached fruit is served with yogurt and a drizzle of honey. You could also serve this as a dessert, as well as a breakfast.

Serves 4 **Prep time** 5 minutes **Cook time** 12 minutes

8 large or 12 small plums, halved and stones removed
Finely grated zest and juice of 1 orange
1 cinnamon stick
4 teaspoons clear honey
120g 0% fat natural Greek yogurt

1 Put the plums into a saucepan and add enough cold water to almost cover them. Add the cinnamon stick, orange zest and juice.

2 Put over a medium heat and bring to the boil, then reduce the heat and simmer for 10-12 minutes until the plums are soft.

3 Serve the plums warm, with a spoonful of the Greek yogurt, and the honey drizzled over.

SmartPoints values per serving 2
SmartPoints values per recipe 8

Breakfast hash with poached eggs

New potatoes, bacon and veg, topped with a perfectly poached egg – this tasty dish makes a great family weekend breakfast.

Serves 4 **Prep time** 10 minutes **Cook time** 30 minutes

250g new potatoes, halved
Calorie controlled cooking spray
150g lean smoked bacon medallions, trimmed of all fat and roughly chopped
1 red onion, sliced
200g mushrooms, sliced
200g cherry tomatoes, larger ones halved
1-2 teaspoons wholegrain mustard
Small handful of fresh flat-leaf parsley, chopped
4 eggs

1 Put the potatoes in a large pan, cover with cold water and bring to the boil. Simmer for 15 minutes, then drain well and set aside.

2 Mist a large nonstick frying pan with cooking spray, add the bacon and cook for 5 minutes. Remove and set aside.

3 Mist the pan again, add the onion and potatoes, then cook for 5 minutes. Add the mushrooms and tomatoes, and cook for another 5 minutes. Season and stir in the mustard, half the parsley and the cooked bacon.

4 Meanwhile, crack the eggs into a pan of simmering water and poach for about 3 minutes until the whites are just set and the yolks are still soft.

5 Divide the hash between 4 plates and top with a poached egg, then season to taste and sprinkle with the remaining parsley.

SmartPoints values per serving 4
SmartPoints values per recipe 16

Oat & banana smoothie

The perfect start to a busy day, this deliciously filling smoothie is topped with caramelised oats.

Serves 2 **Prep time** 5 minutes **Cook time** 3 minutes

40g porridge oats, plus 10g extra for sprinkling (ensure gluten free)
1 teaspoon demerara sugar
Pinch of cinnamon
1 banana
300ml unsweetened soya milk
¼ teaspoon vanilla extract
1 teaspoon honey

1 Dry-fry the extra 10g porridge oats with the demerara sugar and cinnamon in a pan over a medium heat for 2-3 minutes until the oats are toasted and the sugar has caramelised. Remove from the heat and set aside.

2 In a blender, whizz the 40g porridge oats, banana, soya milk, vanilla extract and honey until smooth.

3 Pour the smoothie into the glasses and serve topped with the toasted oat mixture.

SmartPoints values per smoothie 7
SmartPoints values per recipe 14

Mini bagels with smoked salmon spread

Smoked salmon, cream cheese and bagels have always been a match made in heaven – and with added extras, they're even better.

Serves 2 **Prep time** 10 minutes

50g low-fat soft cheese
Zest and juice of ½ lemon
2 teaspoons capers, rinsed and roughly chopped
Small handful of fresh parsley, chopped
A few fresh chives, finely snipped
80g smoked salmon, roughly chopped
4 mini bagels

1 In a bowl, mix together the soft cheese, lemon zest and juice, capers, herbs and salmon. Season to taste, then chill in the fridge until ready to serve.

2 Split and toast the mini bagels, spread with the salmon mixture and serve.

SmartPoints values per serving 9
SmartPoints values per recipe 18

Instead of salmon, you could also use the same quantity of chopped lean ham for no extra SmartPoints.

Sarah's toast toppers

Toast makes a brilliant breakfast for one – it's quick, easy and, with one of these tasty topping ideas, it's delicious too. Here's how to make toast with the most...

'These tasty toasts for one are a great way to use up all those odd bits and pieces you've got in the fridge – and they're ready in next to no time. Mix and match them and you can have a different breakfast every day of the week.' *Sarah*

STEP 1: toast it
A 22g slice of calorie-controlled white or wholemeal bread is just **1 SmartPoint**. Pop it in the toaster while you get the topping ingredients ready.

STEP 2: spread it
If you like, add a level teaspoon of low-fat spread for **1 SmartPoint**.

STEP 3: top it
Add your chosen topping. Forget sugar-laden jams and fatty peanut butter – try these healthier, tastier options. Add the SmartPoints for each one to the toast (these don't include the low-fat spread).

Clockwise from top left

- **50g smoked salmon, cucumber slices – add 2 SmartPoints**
- **40g low-fat cottage cheese, tomatoes, fresh basil – add 1 SmartPoint**
- **Mixed mushrooms sautéed in 1 teaspoon olive oil, rocket leaves – add 2 SmartPoints**
- **2 grilled bacon medallions and ¼ mashed avocado – add 4 SmartPoints**
- **40g ricotta, ½ peach, sliced – add 2 SmartPoints**
- **2 slices wafer-thin ham, 1 sliced boiled egg, snipped chives – add 3 SmartPoints**

Toasty porridge with spiced apple compote

Creamy porridge is topped with spiced stewed apple and yogurt. Toasting the oats first gives the porridge a lovely nutty flavour.

Serves 2 **Prep time** 5 minutes **Cook time** 10 minutes

1 cooking apple, peeled cored and chopped
1 teaspoon lemon juice
1 clove
Small piece of cinnamon stick or a pinch of ground cinnamon
Artificial sweetener, to taste
60g porridge oats (ensure gluten free)
400ml skimmed milk

TO SERVE
Splash of cold skimmed milk
2 heaped teaspoons 0% fat Greek or natural yogurt
Pinch of ground mixed spice

1 Put the apple in a small lidded pan with the lemon juice, a teaspoon of water and the clove and cinnamon. Cover and cook gently for 5 minutes or until the apple starts to break up (add another teaspoon of water if it starts to look dry), then stir in the sweetener. Cover to keep warm.

2 Meanwhile, put the oats in a nonstick pan and toast them over a medium-high heat for a couple of minutes or until fragrant. Add the milk, turn the heat down and slowly bring to the boil, stirring with the handle of a wooden spoon.

3 Simmer on the lowest heat, stirring often, for 8-10 minutes or until cooked and creamy. Spoon into bowls and top with the apple compote and a trickle of cold milk around the edge. Serve with the yogurt and a sprinkle of mixed spice.

SmartPoints values per serving 7
SmartPoints values per recipe 13

Coconut pancakes with tropical fruit

A tropical variation on everyday pancakes, these can be served with whatever fresh fruit you like.

Serves 4 **Prep time** 10 minutes **Cook time** 30 minutes

3 tablespoons desiccated coconut
115g self-raising flour
½ tablespoon caster sugar
½ teaspoon baking powder
200ml coconut drink (we used Alpro Coconut Original)
1 large egg
Calorie controlled cooking spray
200g 0% fat Greek yogurt
1 kiwi fruit, peeled and sliced
100g diced fresh mango
100g diced fresh pineapple,
2 tablespoons pomegranate seeds

1 Put the coconut in a large frying pan over a medium heat and toast for 1-2 minutes, stirring constantly, until it starts to turn golden in colour. Transfer to a bowl to cool.

2 Put the flour, sugar, baking powder and 2½ tablespoons of the toasted coconut in a bowl and stir until combined. In a jug, whisk together the coconut drink and the egg. Add the dry ingredients to the jug and whisk until just combined. Set aside.

3 Mist a large pan with the cooking spray and put over a medium heat. Pour one-eighth of the batter into the pan, swirl the pan to spread out the mixture a little, then cook for 2-3 minutes until the pancake starts to set on top and holes appear. Flip over and cook for a further 2-2½ minutes. Transfer to a plate and repeat to make 8 pancakes.

4 Stack 2 pancakes on top of each other and serve with a dollop of yogurt and a quarter of the fresh fruit, finishing with a sprinkle of the remaining toasted coconut.

SmartPoints values per serving 7
SmartPoints values per recipe 29

Bircher muesli

This fruity no-cook breakfast is the perfect choice if you fancy a lie-in – all the work is done the night before.

Serves 4 **Prep time** 5 minutes plus overnight soaking

150g rolled oats (ensure gluten free)
60g dried apricots, chopped
600ml skimmed milk
200g raspberries

1 Put the oats and apricots in a large bowl and pour the milk over. Stir, cover and refrigerate overnight.

2 Serve the muesli chilled, with the raspberries stirred through.

SmartPoints values per serving 7
SmartPoints values per recipe 29

Potato & bacon frittata

This tasty all-in-one breakfast is also delicious served cold for a weekend brunch or weekday packed lunch.

Serves 2 **Prep time** 10 minutes **Cook time** 20 minutes

100g baby potatoes, sliced
3 eggs
1 tablespoon chopped fresh flat-leaf parsley
Calorie controlled cooking spray
1 red onion, cut into wedges
40g Weight Watchers Extra Trimmed Unsmoked Back Bacon
50g mushrooms, sliced
5 cherry tomatoes, halved

1 Put the potatoes in a pan, cover with cold water and bring to the boil. Cook for 5 minutes until tender. Drain and set aside to cool.

2 Meanwhile, beat the eggs in a bowl with 1 teaspoon cold water and the parsley. Season to taste.

3 Heat a small frying pan over a medium heat and mist with cooking spray. Add the onion and cook for 5 minutes until golden, then transfer to the bowl with the eggs. Fry the bacon in the pan for 1-2 minutes, then add to the bowl.

4 Mist the pan with more spray and cook the mushrooms for 2-3 minutes until tender and golden. Tip them into the bowl, add the cooled potato slices and stir everything together.

5 Return the mixture to the frying pan and cook on a medium heat for 4 minutes. Meanwhile, preheat the grill to medium. Top the frittata with the halved tomatoes and put the pan under the grill for 4-5 minutes, until the egg is set and golden on top.

6 Leave to rest in the pan for 5 minutes (this makes it easier to slice), then slide the frittata onto a board and cut into 4 wedges. Serve 2 wedges per person.

GREAT IDEA
You can use whatever zero SmartPoints vegetables and herbs you have in the fridge.

SmartPoints values per serving 4
SmartPoints values per recipe 8

3 easy muesli ideas

Mix up a batch of this super-simple breakfast muesli, then turn it into delicious on-the-go snacks.

Basic muesli

Serves 10 **Prep time** 5 minutes V GF

In a large bowl, mix 200g **jumbo porridge oats**, 75g **sultanas**, 50g **flaked almonds**, 40g **wheatgerm**, 30g **sunflower seeds** and 25g **golden linseed** together. Store in an airtight container for up to 1 month.

SmartPoints values per serving 6
SmartPoints values per recipe 56

Serve with skimmed milk or unsweetened soya or almond milk.

Even tastier

Want to take your muesli mix to the next flavour level? Sprinkle in 1 teaspoon of mixed spice, matcha green tea or cocoa powder (cocoa adds 1 extra SmartPoint to the recipe).

Muesli bars

Makes 12 **Prep time** 10 minutes
Cook time 45 minutes V GF

Preheat the oven to 150°C, fan 130°C, gas mark 2 and line an 18cm-square baking tin with baking paper. Melt 75g **low-fat spread** in a pan over a low heat. Use a pastry brush to grease the tin with some of the spread. Add 75g **maple syrup** and 75g **Sukrin Gold** sweetener to the pan and heat gently, stirring, until it dissolves. Remove the pan from the heat and stir in 275g of the basic **muesli**, the grated **zest of half a lemon**, ¼ teaspoon **ground ginger** and ¼ teaspoon **cinnamon**. Press the mixture into the tin and bake for 40 minutes. Remove from the oven and cool for 15 minutes, then turn out onto a board and cut into 12 bars.

5 SmartPoints value

SmartPoints values per bar 5
SmartPoints values per recipe 61

Trail mix

Serves 15 **Prep time** 5 minutes
Cook time 45 minutes

Pre-heat the oven to 150°C, fan 130°C, gas mark 2. In a small saucepan over a low heat, melt 60g **coconut oil**. Add 45g **honey** and 1 teaspoon **vanilla extract** and stir until combined. Put 275g of the basic **muesli** in a large bowl, then pour in the coconut oil mixture. Mix together until well combined, then spread out on a large baking tray. Transfer to the oven and bake for 40-45 minutes, stirring every 10 minutes. Remove from the oven and leave to cool, then divide the mix between 15 small plastic ziplock bags (about 25g per bag) and store in an airtight container for up to 1 month for on-the-go snacks.

SmartPoints values per serving 5
SmartPoints values per recipe 78

Muesli muffins

Makes 10 **Prep time** 10 minutes **Cook time** 20 minutes

Preheat the oven to 200°C, fan 180°C, gas mark 6. Line a muffin tin with 10 paper cases. Whisk 1 **egg**, 175g **0% fat natural Greek yogurt**, 1 ripe mashed **banana**, 30g melted **low-fat spread** and 1 tablespoon **honey** together in a jug. In a medium bowl, combine 100g of the basic **muesli**, 45g **plain flour**, 45g **wholemeal flour**, ¼ teaspoon **bicarbonate of soda**, ¼ teaspoon **baking powder** and the **grated zest of half an orange**. Add the wet ingredients to the bowl and mix until just combined. Spoon the mixture into the paper cases and bake for 20 minutes or until golden. While the muffins bake, put 1 tablespoon **honey** and 3 tablespoons **orange juice** in a small saucepan. Heat gently until the honey has melted, then bring to the boil for 2 minutes until reduced slightly. When the muffins are cooked but still warm, brush the honey and orange glaze on with a pastry brush. Cool on a wire rack.

SmartPoints values per muffin 4
SmartPoints values per recipe 41

'Oats are a great ingredient to use in a breakfast or mid-morning snack – their slow-release carbs help you maintain your energy levels throughout the day.' *Sarah*

Lunch

Mozzarella & tomato panzanella

This tomato and bread salad originated in Tuscany and is full of the sun-soaked flavours of the Mediterranean.

Serves 2 **Prep time** 20 minutes, plus resting **Cook time** 8-10 minutes

100g sourdough bread, torn into small chunks
Calorie controlled cooking spray
1 teaspoon dried mixed herbs
300g mixed tomatoes, halved or roughly chopped if large
¼ cucumber, halved length-ways, deseeded and sliced
75g reduced-fat mozzarella, torn
Fresh basil leaves, to serve

FOR THE DRESSING
1 tablespoon extra-virgin olive oil
1 teaspoon white wine vinegar
2 teaspoons freshly squeezed lemon juice
1 tablespoon chopped fresh basil
1 garlic clove, crushed

1 Preheat the oven to 180°C, fan 160°C, gas mark 4. Lightly mist the bread with cooking spray, and put on a baking tray. Scatter over the herbs, season, then bake for 8-10 minutes, until crisp and golden.

2 Combine all the tomatoes with the cucumber in a large bowl. Stir through the baked bread chunks, then leave to sit at room temperature for at least 30 minutes.

3 Meanwhile, make the dressing. Whisk together all the ingredients and season to taste.

4 To serve, scatter the mozzarella and basil over the salad, then drizzle with the dressing.

COOK'S TIP
Use a mixture of Pomodorino, plum and yellow cherry tomatoes in this recipe for extra flavour and colour.

SmartPoints values per serving 10
SmartPoints values per recipe 20

Minestrone soup

For Italians, minestrone means 'big soup' because it's chock-full of vegetables, beans and pasta. Buon appetito!

Serves 6 **Prep time** 15 minutes **Cook time** 35 minutes

1 large onion, chopped
2 garlic cloves, crushed
2 large carrots, chopped
3 celery sticks, sliced thinly
½ swede, chopped
1.5 litres vegetable stock, made with 2 cubes
410g tin borlotti or cannellini beans in water, drained
400g tin chopped tomatoes
1 teaspoon tomato purée
1 tablespoon dried mixed Italian herbs
50g wholewheat spaghetti, broken into short lengths
100g fine green beans, trimmed and sliced
Fresh basil leaves, to garnish

1 Put the onion, garlic, carrots, celery, swede, stock, beans, tomatoes, tomato purée and dried herbs in a large lidded saucepan.

2 Bring to the boil, stirring occasionally. Partially cover, then reduce the heat and simmer for 20-25 minutes, until the vegetables are tender.

3 Add the spaghetti and fine green beans. Stir well, then cook for a further 8-10 minutes, until the pasta is tender. Season, then serve, garnished with basil leaves.

SmartPoints values per serving 2
SmartPoints values per recipe 11

This is a great recipe to batch cook. Freeze single portions in freezer bags for an instant meal when you're busy.

Chicken tikka naan

Chicken tikka should never be off the menu, so spice things up with this Indian-inspired favourite.

Serves 2 **Prep time** 15 minutes, plus marinating **Cook time** 10 minutes

200g skinless chicken breast, cubed
2 teaspoons tikka paste
3 tablespoons low-fat natural yogurt
2 teaspoons mango chutney
2 small reduced-fat naan breads
Small handful of young leaf spinach
Lemon wedges to serve

1 Preheat the grill to high. Mix the chicken breast with the tikka paste and 2 tablespoons of the yogurt, then cover and set aside in the fridge to marinate for 10 minutes.

2 Thread the chicken onto 2 skewers (if you're using wooden skewers, soak them in cold water for 15 minutes beforehand to stop them from burning). Cook under the grill for 10 minutes, turning occasionally.

3 Meanwhile, mix the remaining yogurt with the chutney. Warm the naan breads and spread them with the chutney mixture. Top with the chicken and spinach, then serve with the lemon wedges for squeezing.

SmartPoints values per serving 6
SmartPoints values per recipe 12

COOK'S TIP

To warm the naan, sprinkle with a little water and put in a pan on medium heat for 3 minutes, turning once.

Vietnamese beef pho

The slow-cooked beef in this recipe is meltingly tender and full of flavour – it's well worth the wait!

Serves 4 **Prep time** 15 minutes **Cook time** 1 hour 10 minutes

2 cinnamon sticks
3 whole star anise
2 teaspoons coriander seeds
1 teaspoon fennel seeds
5cm-piece fresh ginger, peeled and finely sliced
1 onion, halved
450g lean braising steak
1 stem lemon grass, trimmed, and tough outer layer removed
1.5 litres hot beef stock, made with 1 stock cube (ensure gluten free)
150g fresh rice noodles
75g beansprouts
4 spring onions, trimmed and sliced on the diagonal
2 red chillies, thinly sliced
Handful of fresh coriander
1 lime, cut into wedges

1 In a heavy-based pot placed over a low-medium heat, dry-fry the cinnamon, star anise, coriander seeds and fennel seeds for 2 minutes until fragrant.

2 Add the ginger and onion to the frying pan and cook for 5-7 minutes, stirring, until charred all over. Add the steak, lemon grass and stock. Cover and simmer gently over a very low heat for about an hour until the beef is very tender. You could also cook this in a slow cooker on low for 4 hours.

3 Lift out the beef, shred and set aside. Strain the broth into a pot, discarding the aromatics and onion. Add the noodles. Steam the beansprouts over a pan of boiling water for 2 minutes.

4 Divide the meat between 4 bowls, then ladle over the noodles and broth. Serve topped with the beansprouts, spring onions, chillies and coriander, with lime wedges for squeezing.

TRY THIS

You can also make this soup using skinless chicken breast meat or prawns instead of beef.

SmartPoints values per serving 7
SmartPoints values per recipe 29

Warm chicken, pancetta & watercress salad

Smoky pancetta adds depth of flavour to this delicious warm chicken and ciabatta crouton salad.

Serves 4 **Prep time** 5 minutes **Cook time** 15 minutes

2 x 165g skinless chicken breasts, halved horizontally
2 tablespoons olive oil
125g ciabatta
2 garlic cloves, 1 halved and 1 crushed
100g diced pancetta
½ red onion, very finely sliced
85g watercress
1 tablespoon Dijon mustard
2 tablespoons cider vinegar
2 tablespoons snipped fresh chives, to garnish

1 Use a rolling pin to flatten the chicken between two pieces of cling film and then brush with half the oil. Heat a griddle pan over a high heat and cook the chicken for 5 minutes on each side.

2 Meanwhile, preheat the oven to 200°C, fan 180°C, gas mark 6. Rub the ciabatta all over with the cut side of the halved garlic clove. Cut into cubes and put on a baking tray. Season and bake for 10-12 minutes, turning halfway, until crisp and golden.

3 While the chicken and croutons are cooking, heat a frying pan over a high heat. Add the pancetta and fry for 5 minutes until crisp and golden. Remove and drain on kitchen paper.

4 Tear the griddled chicken into strips and put in large bowl. Toss together with the pancetta, croutons, red onion and watercress. Divide between 4 plates.

5 Whisk together the mustard, crushed garlic and vinegar. Drizzle over the salad and serve garnished with the chives.

SmartPoints values per serving 9
SmartPoints values per recipe 37

Chicken & avocado wrap with sriracha mayo

The spicy chilli mayonnaise adds a hit of flavour to this classic combination of chicken and avocado in a soft tortilla wrap.

Serves 1 **Prep time** 5 minutes

1 tablespoon light mayonnaise
1 tablespoon sriracha hot chilli sauce
1 Weight Watchers white wrap
75g cooked skinless chicken breast, shredded
30g avocado, peeled, stone removed and sliced
1 tablespoon freshly squeezed lemon juice

1 Put the reduced-fat mayonnaise and the sriracha sauce into a small bowl and mix together until combined.

2 Spread the sriracha mayo onto the tortilla and top with the shredded chicken breast and avocado.

3 Drizzle the lemon juice over the top and roll up the tortilla to serve. For more tasty fillings for wraps, see p78.

SmartPoints values per serving 9
SmartPoints values per recipe 9

Beef pitta pockets

These roast beef pittas get a fantastic flavour boost from chimichurri, a zingy relish made with fresh herbs and chilli.

Serves 2 **Prep time** 10 minutes

2 Weight Watchers High Protein White and Wholemeal Pitta Breads
90g reduced-fat houmous
50g pea shoots, trimmed
½ small red onion, thinly sliced
5 cherry tomatoes, quartered
100g lean roast beef, sliced

FOR THE CHIMICHURRI
Bunch of fresh flat-leaf parsley, leaves picked
Bunch of fresh coriander, leaves picked
2 garlic cloves, crushed
1 tablespoon red wine vinegar
1 tablespoon extra-virgin olive oil
1 teaspoon dried chilli flakes

1 Cut the pitta breads in half and carefully separate the layers to make a pocket. Divide the houmous between them.

2 Make the chimichurri: finely chop the parsley and coriander, and combine with the garlic, vinegar, oil and chilli flakes in a small bowl. Season to taste.

3 Toss the pea shoots, onion, tomatoes, beef and 2 tablespoons of the chimichurri together in a medium bowl. Season to taste. Divide between plates and serve with the pittas. Fill the pittas with the beef and salad before eating.

SmartPoints values per serving 11
SmartPoints values per recipe 22

GREAT IDEA

Keep leftover chimichurri in an airtight container in the fridge and serve with grilled steak, fish or chicken.

Chicken satay noodle salad

The punchy peanut satay dressing is big on flavour and adds a delicious twist to the crunchy veg, chicken and noodles.

Serves 4 **Prep time** 10 minutes **Cook time** 5 minutes

125g soba noodles
300g cooked skinless chicken breast, torn
1 red pepper, deseeded and sliced
2 carrots, peeled and ribboned
120g mangetout
50g young leaf spinach

FOR THE DRESSING
30g reduced-fat peanut butter
1 tablespoon soy sauce (ensure gluten free)
1 tablespoon rice vinegar
Juice of 1 lime
1 tablespoon sweet chilli sauce
1 teaspoon sesame oil

1 Bring a pan of water to the boil and cook the noodles for 3-4 minutes or until tender, then drain and run under cold water.

2 Put the noodles into a bowl and add the torn chicken breast and the vegetables.

3 To make the dressing, whisk together the peanut butter, soy sauce, rice vinegar, lime juice, sweet chilli sauce and sesame oil until smooth. Pour the dressing over the noodles, chicken and veg, and mix until everything is combined.

SmartPoints values per serving 7
SmartPoints values per recipe 28

INSIDE INFO

Soba noodles are made from buckwheat, which is gluten free, but some also contain wheat flour. Check the label.

Baked sweet potato with Asian slaw

This colourful alternative to a jacket potato is topped with a fresh-tasting salad and a zingy Asian-style dressing.

Serves 1 **Prep time** 10 minutes **Cook time** 1 hour

1 medium sweet potato
Calorie controlled cooking spray
1 small carrot, peeled and shredded
¼ white cabbage, shredded
Some fresh ginger, grated
1 red chilli, deseeded and finely chopped
Few fresh coriander leaves, to garnish

FOR THE DRESSING
1 tablespoon 0% fat natural Greek yogurt
Juice of ½ lime
1 teaspoon soy sauce

1 Preheat the oven to 200°C, fan 180°C, gas mark 6. Mist the potato with the cooking spray. Bake for 1 hour until tender.

2 Meanwhile, toss together the carrot, cabbage, ginger and chilli in a bowl. Whisk together the dressing ingredients in a separate bowl and toss through all the vegetables.

3 Cut open the baked sweet potato and serve topped with the slaw and coriander.

SmartPoints values per serving 6
SmartPoints values per recipe 6

COOK'S TIP
There's no need to peel the sweet potato – bake it in its skin as you would an ordinary potato.

Nadine's speedy wraps

Want a healthy lunch you can eat at home or take with you? Nadine's got it all wrapped up – quite literally – with these quick and tasty ideas.

'Why do I love wraps? Well, I can fill them with all those classic sandwich flavour combinations and they're just the right size for a satisfying lunch. Wrap them in tin foil and you can take them anywhere!' *Nadine*

STEP 1: *choose your wrap.*
A Weight Watchers White Wrap is 4 SmartPoints. If you like, warm it in the microwave for 10 seconds, or wrap in foil and heat in the oven for a few minutes.

STEP 2: *fill it.*
Add your chosen filling – try some of the suggestions below and add the SmartPoints. Then wrap them up in foil or cling film and you're good to go.

CLOCKWISE FROM TOP LEFT

- **Roasted butternut squash (see p104), rocket, 40g light feta – add 2 SmartPoints**
- **100g prawns, grated carrot, sliced radishes, fresh coriander and 1 teaspoon sriracha sauce – add 2 SmartPoints**
- **30g houmous, griddled courgette and peppers – add 2 SmartPoints**
- **Cooked asparagus spears, 100g poached salmon, 30g half-fat créme fraîche, grated lemon zest – add 6 SmartPoints**
- **Shredded lettuce, 2 grilled bacon medallions, sliced tomatoes, 1 teaspoon low-fat mayonnaise – add 1 SmartPoint**
- **100g sliced roast beef, sliced red onions, watercress, 1 teaspoon horseradish sauce – add 3 SmartPoints**

Sesame tuna with Japanese-style salad

Sesame, rice wine and wasabi add a whole range of deliciously unique flavours to this East Asian-inspired dish.

Serves 4 **Prep time** 10 minutes **Cook time** 8 minutes

250g microwaveable brown rice
150g green beans, halved
2 tablespoons rice vinegar
1 teaspoon caster sugar
Zest and juice of 1 lime
6 spring onions, trimmed and sliced on the diagonal
½ cucumber, chopped
1 red chilli, thinly sliced
2 tablespoons black sesame seeds
4 x 150g fresh tuna steaks
Calorie controlled cooking spray
3 tablespoons light mayonnaise
1½ teaspoons wasabi paste

1 Cook the rice to the pack instructions, then set aside to cool. Meanwhile, blanch the beans in boiling water for 2-3 minutes in a small bowl. Drain, run under cold water, then drain again.

2 In a second bowl, whisk together the rice vinegar, sugar and lime zest and juice to make a dressing. Season to taste and set aside.

3 Add the cooked beans, spring onions, cucumber and chilli to the cooled rice. Toss with the dressing.

4 Spread the sesame seeds on a plate and press each tuna steak in them to coat. Heat a griddle pan to hot and mist with cooking spray. Sear the tuna for 2 minutes on each side for rare, 3 minutes for medium and 4 minutes for well done.

5 Mix the mayonnaise with the wasabi until combined and serve with the rice salad and tuna.

SmartPoints values per serving 8
SmartPoints values per recipe 31

Turkey banh mi

Banh mi is a popular street food in Vietnam – these wholemeal rolls are filled with poached turkey and lightly pickled vegetables.

Serves 4 **Prep time** 20 minutes **Cook time** 30 minutes

260g turkey breast fillet
2 shallots, peeled and halved
15cm-piece ginger, peeled; ⅔ finely sliced and ⅓ grated
1 teaspoon black peppercorns
2 tablespoons soy sauce
Calorie controlled cooking spray
Zest and juice of 1 lime
2 red chillies, deseeded and chopped
1 garlic clove, crushed
1 tablespoon sesame oil
½ tablespoon rice wine vinegar
3 tablespoons chopped fresh coriander leaves
2 tablespoons chopped fresh mint
¼ cucumber, halved lengthways and thinly sliced
1 carrot, peeled and grated
4 small wholemeal multiseed rolls
2 tablespoons reduced-fat mayonnaise

1 Put the turkey, shallots, sliced ginger and peppercorns in a pan with half the soy sauce. Cover with cold water, bring to a simmer and poach, covered, for 20-25 minutes.

2 Remove the turkey from the pan and discard the poaching liquid. Shred the meat and add to a frying pan misted with cooking spray. Stir in the lime zest, half the chilli and the garlic, then cook over a low heat for 4-5 minutes until just beginning to caramelise.

3 To make the dressing: in a bowl, combine the remaining soy sauce, ginger, lime juice, sesame oil, vinegar, coriander and mint in a bowl. Add the cucumber and carrot and mix.

4 Warm the rolls in the oven, slice open and spread with the mayo. Fill each one with turkey, top with the pickled carrot and cucumber and garnish with the remaining chilli to serve.

TRY THIS

The pickled veg is a traditional ingredient in banh mi. You could also add radish, if you like.

SmartPoints values per serving 7
SmartPoints values per recipe 29

Lamb koftas with fattoush

Fattoush is a simple, versatile and delicious Middle Eastern salad made with fresh vegetables and toasted pitta bread.

Serves 4 **Prep time** 10 minutes **Cook time** 10 minutes

500g lean lamb mince
½ red onion, finely grated
2 garlic cloves, crushed
1 red chilli, deseeded and finely chopped
1 teaspoon ground cumin
1 teaspoon ground cinnamon
Small handful of fresh mint, chopped
100g fat-free natural yogurt
Zest of ½ lemon

FOR THE FATTOUSH
2 Weight Watchers High Protein White and Wholemeal Pitta Breads
Calorie controlled cooking spray
450g cherry tomatoes, halved
½ large cucumber, sliced
½ red onion, thinly sliced
Handful of fresh flat-leaf parsley, chopped
1 teaspoon olive oil
1 teaspoon white wine vinegar
1 teaspoon sumac

1 Preheat the oven to 180°C, fan 160°C, gas mark 4, and the grill to high. To make the koftas, combine all the ingredients except the yogurt and lemon zest, and season. Shape the mixture into 8 equal portions. Run 8 wooden skewers under cold water (to stop them burning); then shape each portion of mince around a skewer. Grill for 8-10 minutes, turning once, until cooked through.

2 Meanwhile, split the pittas in half, put on a baking tray and mist with cooking spray. Bake for 5 minutes or until golden. Cool.

3 Put the tomatoes, cucumber, onion and parsley in a bowl. In a jug, whisk together the oil, vinegar and sumac. Pour over the salad and mix. Break the pittas into pieces and mix into the salad.

4 In a small bowl, mix the yogurt and lemon zest and season well. Serve the koftas with the fattoush and lemon yogurt.

SmartPoints values per serving 11
SmartPoints values per recipe 43

Warm lentil salad with hot-smoked salmon

Known for their distinctive rich, earthy flavour, Puy lentils are the perfect complement to the smoky flavour of the salmon.

Serves 4 **Prep time** 5 minutes **Cook time** 10 minutes

Calorie controlled cooking spray
2 shallots, finely chopped
250g pouch of ready-to-eat Puy lentils
340g hot-smoked salmon fillets, flaked
250g cooked beetroot, diced
70g rocket

FOR THE DRESSING
1 teaspoon extra-virgin olive oil
Juice of ½ lemon
2 tablespoons creamed horseradish sauce
1 tablespoon half-fat crème fraîche

1 Mist a large frying pan with the cooking spray and cook the shallots over a medium heat for 2-3 minutes or until just beginning to soften.

2 Add the lentils and stir well to combine with the shallots. Cook for a further 2 minutes, then gently mix through the salmon and beetroot, cooking for another 2 minutes or until everything is warmed through.

3 Meanwhile, make the dressing. In a small bowl, whisk together the olive oil, lemon juice, horseradish sauce and crème fraîche. Season to taste.

4 Toss the salmon and lentil mixture with the rocket and divide between 4 plates. Serve drizzled with the horseradish dressing.

SmartPoints values per serving 7
SmartPoints values per recipe 29

GREAT IDEA

This can also be served cold – just leave out the rocket and add it in when you're ready to eat.

Tuna & bean salad

Love your lunchtime with this deliciously simple salad – just the thing to help you stay on track.

Serves 2 **Prep time** 10 minutes **Cook time** 9-12 minutes

½ teaspoon cumin seeds
¼ garlic clove
1 tablespoon lemon juice
200g tinned haricot beans, drained and rinsed
1 tablespoon finely chopped fresh parsley
2 eggs
80g green beans, trimmed and halved
100g vacuum-packed beetroot, cut into chunks
1 head romaine lettuce, roughly torn
185g tin tuna in spring water, drained

1 Toast the cumin seeds in a dry frying pan for around 1 minute, or until fragrant. Using a pestle and mortar, crush the cumin seeds and the garlic. Add the lemon juice, mix together, then stir the mixture into the haricot beans, along with the parsley. Season and set aside to let the flavours mingle – the longer the better.

2 Wash the eggs, then boil for 7 minutes, adding the green beans to the pan for the final 2 minutes of cooking. Drain and add the green beans to the haricot bean mixture. Cool the eggs under cold running water, then peel and halve them, and set aside.

3 Toss the beetroot, lettuce and tuna through the beans, then top with the halved eggs and serve.

SmartPoints values per serving 5
SmartPoints values per recipe 10

Mushroom & spinach soup

Packed with loads of fresh spinach and mushrooms, this deliciously creamy soup is big on flavour, small on time.

Serves 4 **Prep time** 10 minutes **Cook time** 20 minutes

25g low-fat spread
1 small onion, finely chopped
450g white mushrooms, finely chopped
2 garlic cloves, crushed
1 tablespoon fresh thyme, chopped
25g plain flour
900ml vegetable stock, made with 2 stock cubes
100g young leaf spinach, roughly chopped, plus a few extra leaves, to serve
150g half-fat crème fraîche

1 Heat the spread in a large nonstick pan over a medium heat, add the onion and cook for 5 minutes until softened and lightly coloured. Add a splash of water if it looks like it may burn. Add the mushrooms, garlic and thyme, then season and cook for a further 10 minutes until all the moisture has cooked off and everything is lightly browned.

2 Add the flour and cook on a low heat for 2 minutes, stirring constantly. Remove from the heat and whisk in the stock. Return to the heat and slowly bring to the boil, stirring all the time. Simmer for 5 minutes.

3 Stir in the chopped spinach and heat for 1 minute until wilted. Remove from the heat and stir in 100g of the crème fraiche. Ladle into warm soup bowls and top with the remaining spinach leaves and crème fraîche, to serve.

SmartPoints values per serving 5
SmartPoints values per recipe 19

Fish tacos

These tasty tacos are the perfect quick-fix meal – soft tortilla wraps are filled with white fish and topped with a fresh tomato salsa.

Serves 2 **Prep time** 10 minutes **Cook time** 5 minutes

2 x 42g Weight Watchers White Wraps
80g green cabbage, finely shredded
1 spring onion, trimmed and sliced
1 tablespoon light mayonnaise
1 tablespoon lime juice, plus extra lime wedges to serve
1 large tomato, chopped
1 tablespoon finely chopped fresh coriander
1 teaspoon chilli sauce
40g avocado, peeled, stone removed and sliced
150g cooked white fish, such as cod

1 Warm the tortillas to pack instructions. Combine the shredded cabbage, spring onion, mayonnaise and lime juice in a small bowl. Season to taste.

2 Mix the tomato, coriander and chilli sauce in another small bowl. Divide the cabbage mixture, tomato mixture, avocado and cooked fish between the tortillas. Cut into halves and serve with the extra lime wedges.

SmartPoints values per serving 7
SmartPoints values per recipe 13

TRY THIS

Instead of fish, you could also make these with 120g cooked prawns for the same SmartPoints.

Four seasons super salad

Salads aren't just for summer – this one made with brown rice, fresh veg and feta is great all year round.

Serves 4 **Prep time** 10 minutes **Cook time** 20 minutes

60g brown rice
150g broccoli florets
2 spring onions, trimmed and thinly sliced
1 carrot, peeled and coarsely grated
½ tablespoon extra-virgin olive oil
2 teaspoons lemon juice, plus 2 lemon wedges, to serve
½ avocado, peeled, stone removed and sliced
40g reduced-fat feta, crumbled
½ teaspoon cumin seeds, toasted and coarsely ground
Freshly snipped salad cress

1 Cook the rice to pack instructions. Drain and rinse under cold running water. Drain well and set aside.

2 Meanwhile, blanch the broccoli in a pan of boiling water for 2 minutes, then rinse under cold running water to cool. Cut into bite-size pieces.

3 Toss the rice with the broccoli, spring onion, carrot, oil and lemon juice. Season then top with the remaining ingredients. Serve with a lemon wedge to squeeze over.

SmartPoints values per serving 4
SmartPoints values per recipe 15

COOK'S TIP

To toast the cumin seeds, put them in a dry frying pan on a medium heat until the fragrance is released.

Courgette & feta fritters

These vegetable cakes are full of summery flavours – serve with a salad and enjoy a taste of sunshine whatever the weather.

Serves 4 **Prep time** 8 minutes **Cook time** 12 minutes

2 medium courgettes, trimmed and coarsely grated
1 medium potato (about 220g), peeled and coarsely grated
50g plain flour
1 egg plus 1 egg yolk, beaten
100g feta, crumbled
Large handful of fresh flat-leaf parsley, roughly chopped
Large handful of fresh dill, roughly chopped
½ teaspoon ground nutmeg
3 tablespoons olive oil
Grated zest and juice of 1 lemon
200g 0% fat natural Greek yogurt
Mixed salad leaves, to serve

1 Pile the grated vegetables on a clean tea towel, make a bundle and squeeze to remove as much excess water as you can – you want the mixture to be as dry as possible.

2 Transfer the vegetables to a large mixing bowl, add the flour and beaten egg and stir to combine. Add the feta, herbs and nutmeg and mix well. Season to taste.

3 Heat the oil in a large, heavy-based frying pan over a medium heat. Carefully drop large spoonfuls of the mixture (four at a time) into the pan, leaving plenty of space between each. Gently flatten the fritters with the back of a spatula and cook for 2 minutes on each side. Remove from the pan and drain on kitchen towels. Repeat with the remaining batter until you have 12 fritters.

4 Mix the lemon zest and juice with the Greek yogurt in a small bowl and season with black pepper. Serve 3 fritters per person, with the salad and yogurt dip on the side.

SmartPoints values per serving 9
SmartPoints values per recipe 36

Pea, asparagus, rocket & halloumi pasta salad

The peppery rocket works well with the distinctive saltiness of the halloumi in this Mediterranean-inspired dish.

Serves 4 **Prep time** 5 minutes **Cook time** 15 minutes

160g spirali pasta
300g asparagus, trimmed and cut into 3cm lengths on the diagonal
160g frozen peas
160g reduced-fat halloumi, sliced
¾ tablespoon red wine vinegar
2 tablespoons extra-virgin olive oil
¼ teaspoon caster sugar
50g rocket

1 Cook the pasta in a pan of boiling water for 8-10 minutes or until al dente. Drain, rinse under cold water, drain again and tip into a large bowl.

2 Meanwhile, cook the asparagus in a pan of boiling water for 2-3 minutes or until tender, adding the peas for the final minute of cooking. Drain, then add the vegetables to the bowl with the pasta.

3 Cook the halloumi in a nonstick frying pan over a high heat for 1-2 minutes on each side or until golden.

4 Whisk together the vinegar, olive oil and sugar. Pour over the pasta and toss well to combine, then stir through the rocket and serve with the halloumi.

SmartPoints values per serving 10
SmartPoints values per recipe 41

GREAT IDEA

To get ahead, prep this up to the end of step 2 the day before serving. Keep in the fridge overnight.

Wholewheat pancakes with creamy leek & ham

These French-style crêpes are topped with a delicious creamy mixture of leeks and ham, flavoured with wholegrain mustard.

Serves 4 **Prep time** 10 minutes, plus chilling **Cook time** 20 minutes

100g wholewheat flour
2 eggs, beaten
300ml semi-skimmed milk
Calorie controlled cooking spray
2 large leeks, trimmed, halved and thinly sliced
200g sliced wafer-thin ham, shredded
1 tablespoon wholegrain mustard
125g low-fat cream cheese
100ml vegetable stock, made from ½ cube

1 Sift the flour into a bowl, add a pinch of salt and make a well in the centre. Gradually pour the eggs into the well in the flour, stirring. Slowly pour in the milk, mixing well until you have a smooth batter. Put in the fridge for 30 minutes to rest.

2 While the batter is resting, mist a large pan with cooking spray, put over a medium-low heat and cook the leeks for around 10 minutes or until softened. Add the ham, mustard, cream cheese and stock, and cook for 1 minute. Season to taste and keep warm.

3 Mist a large nonstick frying pan with cooking spray and put over a medium heat. When the pan is hot, put a quarter of the pancake batter in the pan and swirl so it coats the bottom. Cook for about 2 minutes until set and golden underneath, then flip over and cook for another 30 seconds. Repeat with the remaining batter to make 4 pancakes. Put each one on a plate and divide the filling between them, then serve.

SmartPoints values per serving 7
SmartPoints values per recipe 27

Zesty salmon with fennel & watercress

When you want something quick, colourful and absolutely delicious, this simple no-cook dish is the perfect choice.

Serves 4 **Prep time** 20 minutes

Juice of 2 lemons and zest of 1
1 tablespoon red wine vinegar
1 tablespoon olive oil
300g smoked salmon, torn into strips
1 fennel bulb, trimmed and thinly sliced
100g radishes, trimmed and thinly sliced
½ cucumber, peeled into ribbons
50g watercress leaves
160g rye bread, to serve

FOR THE DRESSING
50ml reduced-fat soured cream
Handful of chopped fresh flat-leaf parsley
4-5 sprigs fresh dill
½ teaspoon Dijon mustard
1 tablespoon lemon juice

1 Whisk together the lemon juice and zest, vinegar and oil in a large bowl. Add the salmon, fennel and radishes, season to taste and toss to combine.

2 In a mini processor, whizz together all of the dressing ingredients with 1 tablespoon water. Add a little extra water if you prefer a thinner dressing.

3 Mix together the cucumber and watercress leaves. Divide between 4 plates and top with the salmon, fennel and radish mixture. Drizzle over the dressing and serve with the rye bread, cut into fingers, on the side.

SmartPoints values per serving 7
SmartPoints values per recipe 29

Instead of rye bread use the same amount of ciabatta and toast or griddle it. Add 2 extra SmartPoints.

3 easy roasted squash ideas

Roasted butternut squash makes a delicious veggie side, but make a double batch of it and you can also use it to make quick and easy lunches.

Roasted butternut squash

Serves 4 **Prep time** 5 minutes **Cook time** 45 minutes V GF

Preheat the oven to 200°C, fan 180°C, gas mark 6. Put 750g peeled, deseeded and cubed **butternut squash** and 4 unpeeled **garlic cloves** on a large roasting tray so that it is spread out and not too close together. Mist with **calorie controlled cooking spray** and season to taste. Roast for 25 minutes, then toss well and roast for another 20 minutes, until the butternut cubes are dark golden and soft.

0 SmartPoints value

SmartPoints values per serving 0
SmartPoints values per recipe 0

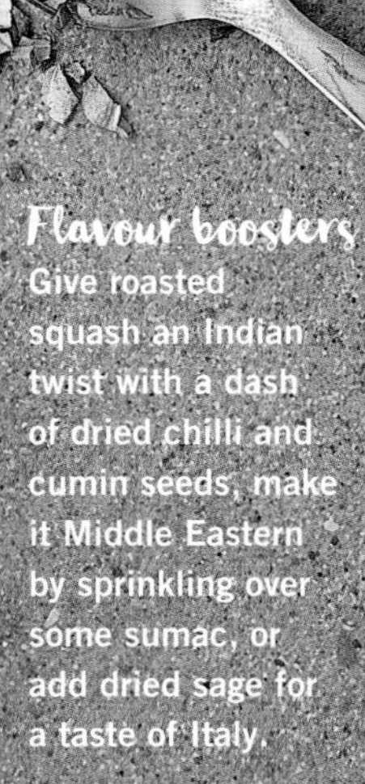

Butternut squash soup

Serves 4 **Prep time** 5 minutes **Cook time** 5 minutes  V GF

Preheat the oven to 200°C, fan 180°C, gas mark 6. Put the whole batch of the **roasted butternut squash** in a blender and add 700ml **vegetable stock** made with 1 gluten-free cube. Blend until you have a smooth soup, then transfer to a pan and place over a medium heat, stirring, until reheated. Season to taste and serve in bowls, swirling 1 teaspoon **low-fat natural yogurt** into each one, to serve.

SmartPoints values per serving 0
SmartPoints values per recipe 1

Flavour boosters

Give roasted squash an Indian twist with a dash of dried chilli and cumin seeds, make it Middle Eastern by sprinkling over some sumac, or add dried sage for a taste of Italy.

Butternut squash & feta salad

Serves 4 **Prep time** 5 minutes
Cook time 2 minutes GF V

Toast 20g **pumpkin seeds** in a dry frying pan over a medium heat for 1-2 minutes until they start to turn golden (take care they don't burn), then remove from the heat and set aside. Put 120g **rocket** into a serving dish and add the whole batch of the **roasted butternut squash** cubes. Crumble over 75g light **feta cheese**. In a small bowl, whisk 2 tablespoons **extra-virgin olive oil** and 1 tablespoon **balsamic vinegar** together. Drizzle the dressing over the salad and top with the toasted pumpkin seeds, then serve.

SmartPoints values per serving 4
SmartPoints values per recipe 17

Butternut squash falafels

Serves 4 **Prep time** 20 minutes
Cook time 40 minutes V GF

Preheat the oven to 220°C, 200°C fan, gas mark 7. Mist a pan with **calorie controlled cooking spray** and cook 1 diced **red onion** on a medium heat for 8-10 minutes, stirring until soft, then put on a plate to cool. Put 2 x 400g tins drained, rinsed **chickpeas** in a food processor and pulse to a chunky purée. Roughly mash the whole batch of the **roasted butternut squash** in a bowl. Add the onion and chickpeas, along with 2 crushed **garlic cloves**, 1½ teaspoons each of **ground cumin** and **coriander**, 1 finely diced **red chilli**, and a handful each of **fresh coriander** and **parsley**, roughly chopped. Shape into 12 balls, then place on a lined baking sheet and chill for 20 minutes. Bake for 20-30 minutes, until golden. Make a sauce to drizzle over the falafels by combining 150g 0% fat natural **Greek yogurt**, 2 teaspoons **lemon juice** and 1 crushed **garlic clove**.

SmartPoints values per serving 4
SmartPoints values per recipe 16

'Roasting squash brings out all it's lovely natural sweetness. As these recipes prove, it's incredibly versatile – it works well with so many other flavours.' *Nadine*

Dinner

Chicken filo pie

This filo-topped chicken and mushroom pie is simple to make and tastes amazing – it's a great dish to serve if you're entertaining.

Serves 4 **Prep time** 15 minutes, plus soaking **Cook time** 55 minutes

10g dried wild mushrooms
400ml hot chicken stock, made with 1 cube
1 tablespoon olive oil
250g chestnut mushrooms, thickly sliced
1 red onion, finely chopped
2 garlic cloves, finely sliced
500g skinless chicken breast, cut into large chunks
2 tablespoons plain flour
2 tablespoons half-fat crème fraîche
3 sheets filo pastry
15g butter, melted
Steamed kale, to serve

1 Put the dried mushrooms in a bowl and pour over the stock. Set aside to soak for 5 minutes until the mushrooms are soft. Meanwhile, heat half the oil in a frying pan and sauté the chestnut mushrooms for 5-10 minutes or until golden. Remove from the pan and set aside.

2 Heat the remaining oil in the pan. Add the onion and garlic and cook for 5 minutes, until softened. Add the chicken and cook for another 5 minutes, until golden on all sides.

3 Stir in the flour and cook for 2 minutes. Slowly add the wild mushrooms and stock. Stir continuously to prevent lumps; leave to simmer for 5-10 minutes or until the sauce starts to thicken.

4 Stir in the crème fraîche and the cooked chestnut mushrooms. Transfer the mixture to a 1.5-litre pie dish and leave to cool slightly.

5 Preheat the oven to 200°C, fan 180°C, gas mark 6. Brush the sheets of pastry with the butter. Scrunch each sheet and lay it on top of the pie filling. Bake for 20 minutes until the filling is bubbling and the pastry is crisp and golden. Serve with the steamed kale.

SmartPoints values per serving 10
SmartPoints values per recipe 36

Tikka-spiced salmon with pilaf

This Indian-inspired salmon dish is easy to make and full of flavour – using ready-cooked rice really cuts down on the cooking time.

Serves 4 **Prep time** 10 minutes **Cook time** 15 minutes

40g tikka paste (ensure gluten free)
30g low-fat natural yogurt
4 x 110g skinless salmon fillets
300g cauliflower, cut into florets
Calorie controlled cooking spray
1 onion, thinly sliced
1 garlic clove, thinly sliced
1 cinnamon stick
6 cardamom pods, crushed
1 teaspoon turmeric
10g toasted flaked almonds
40g raisins
250g pouch ready-cooked basmati rice
100ml vegetable stock made with ½ cube (ensure gluten free)
1 tablespoon chopped fresh coriander
200g young leaf spinach
1 lemon, cut into wedges

1 Preheat the oven to 200°C, fan 180°C, gas mark 6. Mix the tikka paste and yogurt together, rub it all over the salmon, then put the fish, onto a foil-lined baking tray and cook for 15 minutes.

2 Meanwhile, put the cauliflower in a pan of boiling water and, cook for 5 minutes, then drain and set aside.

3 Mist a pan with the cooking spray and cook the onion for 5 minutes over a medium heat. Add the garlic and spices, and cook for 1 minute. Stir in the almonds, raisins, rice, cauliflower and stock. Cook, stirring, for a few minutes or until the stock has been absorbed. Stir in the coriander and spinach to wilt, and season. Serve with the salmon and lemon wedges.

SmartPoints values per serving 10
SmartPoints values per recipe 40

Chicken & mushroom masala

Put away those takeaway menus and enjoy this aromatic, healthy, home-cooked curry instead.

Serves 2 **Prep time** 5 minutes **Cook time** 35 minutes

2 x 125g skinless chicken breasts
2 teaspoons garam masala
1 teaspoon ground coriander
1 teaspoon ground cumin
1 red chilli, deseeded and finely chopped
3 garlic cloves, crushed
2cm-piece fresh ginger, grated
Calorie controlled cooking spray
1 onion, sliced
250g mushrooms, sliced
400g tin cherry tomatoes
100g brown rice
Small handful of fresh coriander leaves
4 tablespoons 0% fat natural Greek yogurt

1 Make slashes in the chicken breasts. Mix the spices, chilli, garlic and ginger with 1 teaspoon cold water to make a paste. Rub into the chicken and set aside.

2 Mist a nonstick frying pan with cooking spray and place over a medium heat, then add the onion and cook for 5 minutes. Add the mushrooms, fry for 5 minutes, then add the chicken and cook for a further 5 minutes, turning once. Add the tomatoes with 2 tablespoons water. Cover and simmer over a low heat for 15 minutes. Remove the lid, turn the chicken breasts over and let the sauce reduce for 3 minutes.

3 Meanwhile, cook the rice to pack instructions. Finely chop half of the coriander and stir into the yogurt. Slice the chicken breasts.

4 Divide the rice between 2 plates and top with the curry sauce, sliced chicken and a spoonful of the coriander yogurt, then sprinkle over the remaining coriander leaves.

SmartPoints values per serving 8
SmartPoints values per recipe 15

Spicy stir-fried beef & broccoli with carrot noodles

Get inspired with this easy beef stir-fry and increase your veg intake with some colourful carrot noodles.

Serves 4 **Prep time** 10 minutes **Cook time** 15 minutes

200g Tenderstem broccoli
Calorie controlled cooking spray
1 red onion, finely sliced
2 garlic cloves, finely sliced
2 x 225g lean sirloin steaks, cut into thin strips
1 tablespoon sesame oil
1 tablespoon soy sauce (ensure gluten-free)
2 teaspoons sriracha hot chilli sauce
1 tablespoon clear honey
30g cashews, roughly chopped
500g carrots, peeled and spiralised
Small handful of fresh coriander, chopped
1 lime, cut into wedges

1 Put the broccoli in a large pan of water, bring to the boil and cook for 2 minutes or until just tender. Drain and set aside.

2 Mist a wok with cooking spray, cook the onion and garlic over a medium heat for 6-8 minutes until soft. Turn up the heat and add the steak. Stir-fry for 2 minutes until browned all over. Reduce the heat to medium, then add the broccoli, sesame oil, soy sauce, sriracha sauce and honey. Toss to heat through. In a separate pan, toast the cashews for 2-3 minutes until golden.

3 Meanwhile, put the carrot 'noodles' in a pan and add 100ml water. Cook over a medium heat for 3-4 minutes until the water has evaporated and the 'noodles' are tender, but still retaining a bit of bite. Add more water if needed. Divide the carrot noodles between 4 bowls and top with the stir-fry. Sprinkle over the cashews and serve with the coriander and lime wedges.

SmartPoints values per serving 7
SmartPoints values per recipe 28

Peanut pork with wild rice

This Asian-inspired dish is full of flavour – and if you marinate the pork overnight you'll add even more!

Serves 4 **Prep time** 15 minutes, plus marinating
Cook time 50 minutes

50g reduced-fat peanut butter
3 tablespoons soy sauce (ensure gluten free)
1 large garlic clove, crushed
5cm-piece ginger, grated
350g lean pork loin steak, diced
160g wild rice
100g frozen peas
Calorie controlled cooking spray
1 red and 1 green pepper, each deseeded and sliced
1 red chilli, deseeded and sliced
4 spring onions, trimmed and sliced
Lime wedges, to serve

1 Combine the peanut butter, soy sauce, garlic and ginger in a bowl. Add the pork and turn to coat, then cover and put in the fridge to marinate for at least 30 minutes or overnight if you can.

2 Cook the rice according to pack instructions, adding the peas for the last 2 minutes of the cooking time.

3 Meanwhile, mist a frying pan with the cooking spray and heat over a medium heat. Add the pork and fry for 3-4 minutes, add the peppers and a splash of water and cook for another 3-4 minutes, until the pork is cooked through.

4 Serve the rice and peas with the pork, garnished with the chilli and spring onions, with lime wedges on the side.

SmartPoints values per serving 11
SmartPoints values per recipe 42

Prawn, red lentil & cauliflower curry

With its delicious and unique South-East Asian flavouring, this speedy curry makes a great mid-week dinner.

Serves 4 **Prep time** 10 minutes **Cook time** 20 minutes

1 tablespoon olive oil
1 onion, thinly sliced
2 garlic cloves, chopped
2cm-piece fresh ginger, chopped
20g rogan josh paste (ensure gluten free)
400g tin chopped tomatoes
400ml vegetable stock, made with 1 cube (ensure gluten free)
100g split red lentils
300g small cauliflower florets
300g raw king prawns
100g young leaf spinach
Small handful of fresh coriander, chopped
80g low-fat natural yogurt

1 Heat the oil in a pan over a medium-low heat, add the onion, garlic and ginger and cook for 5 minutes. Add the rogan josh paste, the chopped tomatoes, stock and the red lentils. Bring to a simmer, then add the cauliflower florets and cook for 15 minutes.

2 Stir in the prawns and spinach, for the last 3 minutes of cooking time, then season to taste.

3 Stir half of the coriander through the curry, then serve garnished with the remaining chopped coriander and a dollop of yogurt.

SmartPoints values per serving 5
SmartPoints values per recipe 21

GREAT IDEA

You could serve the curry with 120g cooked brown rice per person, for an extra 4 SmartPoints per serving.

Bibimbap

Korean in origin, bibimbap is a one-bowl dish of rice and vegetables topped with an egg and meat or tofu – here we've used lean turkey.

Serves 4 **Prep time** 10 minutes **Cook time** 15 minutes

125g long-grain rice
1 tablespoon toasted sesame oil
150g carrots, peeled and cut into matchsticks
120g shiitake mushrooms, sliced
1 large courgette, diced
200g beansprouts
200g young leaf spinach
250g lean turkey mince
1 tablespoon soy sauce (ensure gluten-free)
1 tablespoon rice vinegar
4 eggs
2 tablespoons chilli sauce (ensure gluten-free), to serve

1 Rinse the rice under cold water until the water runs clear. Transfer to a pan; cover with 250ml cold water. Bring to the boil, then reduce to a simmer. Cover and cook for 12 minutes. Remove from the heat for 5 minutes. Fluff up the grains of rice with a fork.

2 Meanwhile, heat half the sesame oil in a large wok or frying pan over a medium-high heat. Add the carrots and mushrooms and stir-fry for 3-4 minutes. Remove from the wok with a slotted spoon. Stir-fry the courgette and beansprouts for 3-4 minutes, then return the carrots and mushrooms to the wok. Stir in the spinach to wilt, then season to taste.

3 Meanwhile, heat the remaining oil in another frying pan and cook the turkey over a medium-high heat for 3-5 minutes or until cooked through. Stir in the soy sauce, vinegar and cooked veg.

4 Poach the eggs in a pan of simmering water for 2-3 minutes for a slightly runny yolk. Divide the rice between 4 bowls. Top with the vegetables and turkey, a poached egg and a drizzle of chilli sauce.

SmartPoints values per serving 8
SmartPoints values per recipe 30

Chilli & tomato tagliatelle

With its classic flavours of tomato, chilli and asparagus, this pasta dish is not only quick and easy to make, it's extremely tasty, too.

Serves 4 **Prep time** 10 minutes **Cook time** 15 minutes

450g asparagus, trimmed
Calorie controlled cooking spray
250g tagliatelle
300g passata
16 cherry or baby plum tomatoes, halved
1 red or green chilli, deseeded and finely chopped
20g hard Italian cheese, grated
Fresh basil leaves, to garnish

1 Preheat a griddle pan over a medium heat. Mist the asparagus with the cooking spray and griddle in batches for 5 minutes, turning occasionally, until tender.

2 Meanwhile, cook the tagliatelle in a pan of boiling water for 10-12 minutes, or according to pack instructions, until tender.

3 Drain the pasta and set aside. Add the passata, tomatoes and chilli to the hot pan. Bring to the boil, then return the tagliatelle to the pan. Stir everything together gently and season to taste.

4 Top with the griddled asparagus, sprinkle with the grated cheese and scatter over the basil leaves, to serve.

SmartPoints values per serving 7
SmartPoints values per recipe 27

DINNER

Spicy turkey burger with rosemary & garlic wedges

For a great-tasting burger and chips that beats a takeaway hands down, try this easy recipe for one.

Serves 1 **Prep time** 15 minutes **Cook time** 40 minutes

Calorie controlled cooking spray
1 potato, skin on
1 teaspoon dried rosemary
1 teaspoon garlic granules
140g turkey breast mince
½ teaspoon wholegrain mustard
½ teaspoon English mustard
½ teaspoon smoked paprika
½ teaspoon chilli flakes
1 brown sandwich thin
Handful of fresh rocket
2 slices of beef tomato
½ small red onion, thinly sliced
2 small gherkins, sliced lengthways
2 teaspoons sriracha hot chilli sauce

1 Preheat the oven to 200°C, fan 180°C, gas mark 6. Mist a baking tray with cooking spray. Scrub the potato and pat dry with kitchen paper. Leaving the skin on, cut it into wedges and put in a bowl. Mist with the cooking spray and sprinkle over the rosemary and garlic granules, then mix until evenly coated. Transfer to the prepared tray and bake for 35-40 minutes, turning halfway.

2 Meanwhile, put the mince, mustards, paprika and chilli in a bowl, season and mix well, then shape into a burger. Heat a nonstick pan over a medium heat, mist with cooking spray, add the burger and fry for 6 minutes on each side until cooked through.

3 Meanwhile, split the sandwich thin and put some rocket and tomato on the bottom half. Spoon on the chilli sauce. Top with the burger, more tomato, the onion and gherkins and more rocket. Finish with the other sandwich thin half and serve with the wedges.

SmartPoints values per serving 11
SmartPoints values per recipe 11

Aubergine lasagne

Replacing pasta with slices of griddled aubergine means you can still enjoy a rich lasagne while keeping the SmartPoints down.

Serves 4 **Prep time** 20 minutes **Cook time** 1 hour 20 minutes

Calorie controlled cooking spray
3 large aubergines, cut lengthways into ½cm slices
1 onion, finely chopped
2 garlic cloves, crushed
1 large carrot, peeled and diced
250g mushrooms, finely chopped
2 teaspoons dried mixed herbs
500g 5% fat beef mince
1 tablespoon tomato purée
2 x 400g tins chopped tomatoes
150g reduced-fat mozzarella, torn
25g mature Cheddar, grated
Basil leaves, to serve

1 Mist a griddle pan with cooking spray, add the aubergine slices and cook over a high heat on both sides until chargrilled. Set aside.

2 Mist a large pan with cooking spray. Add the onion and garlic, and cook for 2-3 minutes until soft. Add the carrot and mushrooms; cook for a further 2-3 minutes, stirring occasionally. Sprinkle the herbs on top, then add the mince to the pan, breaking it up with a wooden spoon. Cook for 3-4 minutes until the mince has browned all over. Stir in the tomato purée and cook for 1 minute. Add the tomatoes and bring to the boil, then simmer for 10 minutes.

3 Preheat the oven to 200°C, fan 180°C, gas mark 6. Spoon a third of the meat sauce over the base of a 20cm ovenproof dish. Top with a third of the aubergine slices, then a third of the mozzarella. Repeat the process twice more, finishing with a layer of mozzarella, then scatter over the Cheddar.

4 Bake for 35-45 minutes, until the top is golden and bubbling. Cool slightly, then garnish with basil leaves, to serve.

TRY THIS

Using 8 sheets of lasagne pasta, instead of aubergine, will make this 10 SmartPoints per serving.

SmartPoints values per serving 6
SmartPoints values per recipe 24

Cottage pie with sweet potato topping

Swapping regular mash for colourful sweet potato gives an interesting taste twist to this family classic.

Serves 4 **Prep time** 15 minutes **Cook time** 1 hour

Calorie controlled cooking spray
1 onion, sliced
2 garlic cloves, crushed
2 carrots, peeled and diced
2 celery sticks, chopped
2 sprigs fresh thyme, leaves picked
500g 5% fat beef mince
230g tin chopped tomatoes
1 tablespoon Worcestershire sauce
550ml hot beef stock, made with 1 cube
800g sweet potatoes, peeled and roughly chopped
2 tablespoons skimmed milk
150g frozen peas

1 Mist a large pan with cooking spray, add the onion and fry over a medium heat for 5-6 minutes until soft. Add the garlic and cook for another minute. Add the carrots and celery, then season and cook for 5-6 minutes until just tender. Add the thyme, then the beef mince, using a wooden spoon to break it up. Cook for 5-6 minutes until the mince has browned all over.

2 Add the tomatoes, Worcestershire sauce and stock. Bring to the boil and simmer gently for 20 minutes until the sauce has reduced and most of the liquid should have evaporated.

3 Meanwhile, preheat the oven to 200°C, fan 180°C, gas mark 6. Bring a large pan of water to the boil and cook the sweet potatoes for 15 minutes. Drain, mash with the milk, then season. Stir the peas through the mince, then spoon into 4 individual pie dishes, or 1 large dish. Top with the mash and bake for 20-25 minutes until the topping has browned and the mince is bubbling.

SmartPoints values per serving 11
SmartPoints values per recipe 44

DINNER

Butternut squash & pancetta cakes

Mashed squash and potatoes make a great base for these cakes, which are flavoured with pancetta, shallots and thyme.

Serves 4 **Prep time** 10 minutes **Cook time** 1 hour 10 minutes

1 small butternut squash
2 medium baking potatoes
Calorie controlled cooking spray
2 banana shallots, finely chopped
70g pancetta, diced
2 cloves garlic, crushed
1 egg, lightly beaten
100g plain flour
4 sprigs fresh thyme, leaves picked
1 tablespoon grated Parmesan
80g watercress
3 tablespoons reduced-fat crème fraîche

1 Preheat the oven to 220°C, fan 200°C gas mark 7. Halve the squash lengthways and scoop out the seeds. Cut a cross into the potatoes. Put both veg on a baking tray, mist with cooking spray and cook for 1 hour, until soft. Cool slightly, then scoop out the flesh from the butternut squash (you'll need 400g) and the potato (you'll need 250g). Mash both together in a bowl, then set aside to cool.

2 Meanwhile, heat a small nonstick frying pan over a medium heat and mist with cooking spray. Add three-quarters of the chopped shallots, the pancetta and the garlic, and cook for 5 minutes until the shallots have softened.

3 Add the pancetta and onion to the mashed veg, along with the beaten egg, flour, thyme and Parmesan. Mix well, then form into 8 flat cakes. Mist a nonstick pan with cooking spray and cook the cakes for 4-5 minutes on each side until they're golden brown. Serve with the watercress, remaining chopped shallots and a spoonful of créme fraîche.

SmartPoints values per serving 9
SmartPoints values per recipe 36

Harissa salmon with cauliflower tabbouleh

Using cauliflower in place of traditional bulgar wheat makes this spicy recipe gluten free and lower in SmartPoints, too.

Serves 4 **Prep time** 10 minutes **Cook time** 20 minutes

4 x 130g skinless salmon fillets
2 tablespoons harissa paste
Juice of 1 lemon, plus extra lemon wedges to serve
200g cauliflower florets
Calorie controlled cooking spray
6 tablespoons chopped fresh flat-leaf parsley
4 tablespoons chopped fresh mint
1 tablespoon red wine vinegar
1 tablespoon extra-virgin olive oil
150g tomatoes, chopped
½ bunch spring onions, trimmed and finely sliced
3 courgettes, trimmed and thinly sliced lengthways

1 Preheat the oven to 180°C, fan 160°C, gas mark 4. Put each salmon fillet onto a large square of foil, spread over the harissa paste and drizzle with half the lemon juice. Fold the foil into loose parcels; bake for 18-20 minutes, until the fish is cooked through.

2 Meanwhile, blitz the cauliflower in a food processor until it looks like couscous. Mist a nonstick frying pan with cooking spray, add the cauliflower and cook over a medium heat for 4-5 minutes, then remove from the heat and mix in the herbs, vinegar, oil, remaining lemon juice, tomatoes and most of the spring onions.

3 Mist a griddle pan with the cooking spray and cook the courgette over a high heat for about 30 seconds on each side.

4 Serve the fish with the tabbouleh and courgette, garnished with the remaining spring onions and lemon wedges.

COOK'S TIP

Harissa is a great flavour booster, so keep a jar handy in your fridge and add to fish or veg before roasting.

SmartPoints values per serving 7
SmartPoints values per recipe 26

Mushroom & spinach risotto

The dried wild mushrooms are the secret ingredient in this dish, adding a wonderful earthy flavour to this creamy risotto.

Serves 4 **Prep time** 15 minutes, plus soaking
Cook time 15-20 minutes

10g dried wild mushrooms
1 litre hot vegetable stock, made with 1 cube (ensure gluten free)
2 teaspoons olive oil
1 red onion, finely chopped
2 garlic cloves, thinly sliced
300g risotto rice
500g mixed fresh mushrooms (such as chestnut, oyster and shiitake), roughly chopped
150g young leaf spinach
30g vegetarian hard cheese, grated

1 Put the dried mushrooms in a bowl, pour over all the hot stock and set aside to soak for 5 minutes, then remove the mushrooms from the stock with a slotted spoon and roughly chop. Strain the stock and keep it hot – you will need it for making the risotto.

2 Heat 1 teaspoon of the oil in a frying pan, add the onion and garlic, then cook for 2 minutes until soft.

3 Stir in the rice, three-quarters of the hot stock and the dried mushrooms. Reduce to a simmer and cook for 12-15 minutes, stirring occasionally. When the stock is almost all absorbed, taste the rice. If it is not cooked, add the remaining stock and continue cooking until the rice is al dente.

4 Meanwhile, heat the remaining oil in a separate pan, add the mixed fresh mushrooms and cook for 10 minutes. Season to taste. Stir the spinach and hard cheese into the risotto, then serve topped with the fresh mushrooms.

INSIDE INFO
It's important to use risotto rice – its high starch content gives the dish its hallmark creamy texture.

SmartPoints values per serving 10
SmartPoints values per recipe 40

DINNER

Roast chicken with grapes

The sweetness of the grapes is a delicious flavour addition to succulent roast chicken seasoned with rosemary and tarragon.

Serves 6 **Prep time** 10 minutes
Cook time 1 hour 15 minutes, plus resting

4 sprigs fresh rosemary
1 tablespoon olive oil
1 garlic clove, crushed
1.5kg chicken, patted dry with kitchen paper
1 lemon, halved
3 shallots, roughly chopped
Small handful fresh tarragon
900g mixed grapes (green, red and black)
720g boiled new potatoes and 480g steamed broccoli, to serve

1 Preheat the oven to 200°C, fan 180°C, gas mark 5. Roughly chop the leaves from 2 of the rosemary sprigs and mix with half the oil and the garlic, and season well. Rub over the chicken and transfer to a roasting tin.

2 Put the lemon, shallots, remaining rosemary sprigs and the tarragon in the cavity and tie the chicken legs with kitchen string. Roast for 45 minutes.

3 Meanwhile, toss the grapes in the remaining oil and season – it's okay to leave them bunched. Remove the chicken from the oven and add the grapes to the tin. Return the tin to the oven to roast for a further 20-30 minutes, basting halfway through, until the chicken is cooked through and the grapes are sticky.

4 Remove from the oven and leave to rest for 15 minutes before carving. Serve each person 80g chicken with some grapes, boiled new potatoes and steamed broccoli.

SmartPoints values per serving 5
SmartPoints values per recipe 32

Crab, chilli & tomato linguine

Create an impressive and easy restaurant-style seafood supper using tinned crab meat and dried pasta.

Serves 4 **Prep time** 10 minutes **Cook time** 10 minutes

250g linguine (see Cook's tip)
Calorie controlled cooking spray
1 garlic clove, crushed
1 red chilli, deseeded and chopped
335g cherry tomatoes, halved
2 x 170g tins white crab meat, drained
Zest and juice of 1 lemon
1 tablespoon extra-virgin olive oil
1 tablespoon finely chopped fresh flat-leaf parsley

1 Put the pasta in a large pan of boiling water. Bring back to the boil and simmer for 6-7 minutes, or until the linguine is al dente. Drain, reserving a little of the pasta cooking water.

2 Meanwhile, mist a large pan with cooking spray, add the garlic and chilli and cook over a medium heat for 1-2 minutes. Add the tomatoes and cook for another 3-4 minutes until they begin to break down. Gently stir in the crab meat, lemon juice and olive oil until combined.

3 Add a couple of tablespoons of the reserved pasta water to the sauce, then add the cooked linguine, tossing everything together until well combined.

4 Divide between bowls and serve garnished with the lemon zest and parsley.

SmartPoints values per serving 8
SmartPoints values per recipe 30

COOK'S TIP

To make this recipe No Count, use wholewheat pasta and leave out the olive oil.

Sarah's No Count bowl food

If you haven't got into bowl food – now's the time to start. It's quick, tasty and healthy, and you can put together endless combinations using ingredients from the No Count food list...

'This is a great way to make a meal if you're following No Count. Choose foods from the No Count food list and you don't have to worry about measuring, weighing or sticking to a recipe. Just dig out your favourite bowl and follow this easy guide.'
Sarah

STEP 1: *start with greens*
Put a couple of handfuls of green leafy veg in your bowl – try kale, rocket, watercress, spinach, Savoy cabbage or Swiss chard.

STEP 2: *go with the grain*
Add a scoop of cooked grains – try cooking them in stock, or add spices to the cooking water to give them extra flavour. Quinoa, brown rice, wild rice, buckwheat, bulgar wheat, freekeh, wholewheat couscous, spelt and millet are all No Count.

STEP 3: *add more veg*
Pile on a variety of veg – as much as you like. Go for different textures, colours and flavours – choose whatever combinations appeal to you.

STEP 4: *pack in some protein*
Add your protein – it could be lean meat, fish or poultry, or vegetarian. Try tofu, beans, chickpeas or pulses, boiled or poached egg, poached salmon, tinned tuna, cooked skinless chicken breast, bacon medallions, extra-lean mince (stir-fried with spices) – they're all on the No Count food list.

STEP 5: *drizzle on the dressing*
Drizzle over a healthy dressing, made using No Count ingredients and extras from the flavour boosters list. Try mixing crushed garlic, freshly grated ginger, fish sauce and lime juice. Or make a yogurt-based dressing using fat-free natural yogurt – whizz it with some lemon juice and fresh herbs, or mix it with wholegrain mustard, harissa paste or tomato purée.

STEP 6: *finishing touches*
Garnish with fresh herbs, alfalfa sprouts, lemon zest or a sprinkling of spices such as paprika or sumac.

Fish pie

A much-loved classic. Tender fish in a creamy sauce under a comforting blanket of fluffy mash – make it in advance and eat at your leisure.

Serves 4 **Prep time** 10 minutes **Cook time** 45 minutes

700g potatoes, cubed
2 tablespoons semi-skimmed milk
2 teaspoons Dijon mustard
15g low-fat spread
15g plain flour
300ml vegetable stock, made with ½ cube
3 tablespoons half-fat crème fraîche
1 tablespoon chopped fresh dill
Calorie controlled cooking spray
450g skinless mixed fish fillets, cut into chunks
150g frozen peas
15g parmesan, grated
Steamed vegetables and lemon wedges, to serve

1 Preheat the oven to 180°C, fan 160°C, gas mark 4.

2 Cook the potatoes in a pan of boiling water for 15 minutes or until soft. Remove from the heat and drain, then mash roughly with a potato masher, adding the semi-skimmed milk. Stir through the mustard, then season and set aside.

3 Melt the low-fat spread in a pan and heat until foaming. Stir in the flour to form a paste and cook over a gentle heat for 1-2 minutes, before slowly adding the stock. Do this a little at a time, whisking well, so there are no lumps. Once you have a smooth sauce, simmer for 5 minutes until thickened. Remove from the heat and stir through the crème fraîche and dill. Season to taste.

4 Mist a 1.5-litre pie dish with cooking spray. Add the fish and peas to the sauce and stir gently to combine, then tip into the pie dish. Top with the mashed potato, scatter over the parmesan and bake for 20 minutes until golden and bubbling. Serve with the steamed veg and lemon wedges.

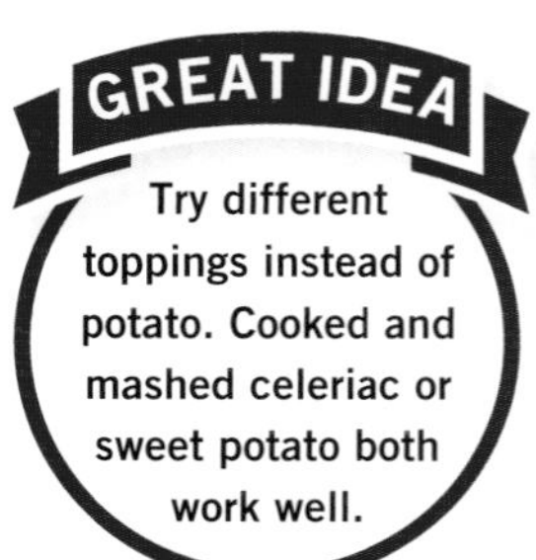

SmartPoints values per serving 13
SmartPoints values per recipe 51

Bacon & cabbage pasta

A simple pasta dish with a classic flavour combination, this makes a really quick and easy midweek meal.

Serves 4 **Prep time** 10 minutes **Cook time** 15 minutes

Calorie controlled cooking spray
200g smoked bacon medallions, finely sliced
1 white onion, finely sliced
3 garlic cloves, sliced
1 Savoy cabbage, outer leaves removed, cored and sliced
150ml vegetable stock, made with ½ cube
240g wholewheat spaghetti
200g young leaf spinach
4 tablespoons 0% fat natural Greek yogurt

1 Mist a large pan with cooking spray and put over a medium heat. Add the bacon and fry for 5 minutes until crisp. Add the onion and cook for a further 5 minutes or until the onion has started to soften.

2 Add the garlic and cook for 1 minute, then add the cabbage and cook for 3 minutes. Pour in the stock and cook until the cabbage is just tender – this should only take about 2 minutes.

3 Meanwhile, bring a large pan of water to the boil. Add the spaghetti and cook for 10-12 minutes until al dente. Drain, reserving a little of the pasta water.

4 Stir the spinach through the cabbage and bacon to wilt, followed by the yogurt and a little pasta water to loosen. Season to taste and cook for a few minutes until thickened slightly. Toss with the spaghetti and serve.

SmartPoints values per serving 7
SmartPoints values per recipe 28

COOK'S TIP

Don't overcook the cabbage or you'll lose its fresh flavour. It should be just tender, but still have some bite.

DINNER

Moroccan beef-stuffed aubergines

Dried apricots add a little sweetness to the filling of this Middle Eastern dish, while the harissa gives it a spicy kick.

Serves 4 **Prep time** 10 minutes **Cook time** 1 hour

4 large aubergines
2 garlic cloves, one whole and one crushed
½ tablespoon olive oil
Calorie controlled cooking spray
1 onion, finely chopped
1 teaspoon ground cumin
1 teaspoon ground coriander
250g 5% fat beef mince
2 tablespoons harissa
6 large tomatoes, chopped
50g dried apricots, chopped
75g half-fat Cheddar, grated
Chopped fresh parsley, to serve

1 Preheat the oven to 200°C, fan 180°C, gas mark 6. Cut the aubergines in half lengthways, then score the flesh deeply all over with a knife. Cut the whole garlic clove in half and rub the flesh of the aubergines with the cut side, then drizzle with olive oil. Put on 2 baking trays and bake for 40-45 minutes until soft.

2 Meanwhile, mist a large pan with cooking spray. Add the onion and cook over a medium heat for 4-5 minutes until soft, then add the crushed garlic and cook for another minute.

3 Stir in the spices and cook for 1 minute, then add the mince. Cook, stirring, for 7-8 minutes until browned. Stir in the harissa, tomatoes and apricots and cook for 1 minute.

4 Once the aubergines are cooked, carefully remove most of the flesh, leaving the skins with a 1cm layer. Chop the removed aubergine and stir it into the pan, then spoon the mixture into the aubergine cases.

5 Sprinkle with the Cheddar cheese and bake for 8-10 minutes, until the cheese is golden and bubbling. Serve sprinkled with the chopped parsley.

SmartPoints values per serving 5
SmartPoints values per recipe 20

Crumbed cod with warm potato salad

Forget fish and chips – this healthier fish supper uses fresh herbs, lemon and garlic for a super-fresh tasting meal.

Serves 4 **Prep time** 15 minutes **Cook time** 20 minutes

100g ciabatta
1 tablespoon each chopped fresh mint, basil and flat-leaf parsley
1 garlic clove, minced
Zest of ½ lemon
1 tablespoon extra-virgin olive oil
4 x 180g pieces skinless cod loin

FOR THE POTATO SALAD
600g baby potatoes, halved
100g frozen peas
3 spring onions, trimmed and sliced on the diagonal
1 tablespoon chopped fresh flat-leaf parsley
1 tablespoon wholegrain mustard
1 tablespoon lemon juice

1 Preheat the oven to 200°C, fan 180°C, gas mark 6. Tear the ciabatta into chunks and blitz in a food processor until you have coarse crumbs. Add the herbs, garlic, lemon zest and oil. Season to taste. Pulse to combine and set aside.

2 Meanwhile, put the potatoes in a large pan of water, bring to the boil and cook for 12 minutes. Add the peas, and cook for a further 4 minutes. Drain and set aside.

3 Meanwhile, season the fish to taste and put on a foil-lined baking tray. Top each piece with a quarter of the crumb mixture, patting it down to form a crust. Bake for 12 minutes or until the fish is opaque and flakes easily.

4 Put the potatoes, peas, spring onions and parsley in a large salad bowl. Whisk together the mustard and lemon juice and drizzle over the potato mixture. Toss to combine and serve alongside the fish.

SmartPoints values per serving 8
SmartPoints values per recipe 32

Turkey & fennel hotpot

Thanks to some clever ingredient swaps, this creamy and indulgent looking hotpot is lighter than you might think.

Serves 6 **Prep time** 20 minutes **Cook time** 1 hour 25 minutes

Calorie controlled cooking spray
1 onion, finely chopped
250g mushrooms, quartered
450g potatoes, cubed
1 fennel bulb, trimmed and thinly sliced
2 teaspoons dried mixed herbs
600g skinless roast turkey, roughly chopped
1 tablespoon plain flour
150g low-fat soft cheese
2 tablespoons wholegrain mustard
4 tablespoons half-fat crème fraîche
450ml hot vegetable stock, made with 1 cube
1 medium butternut squash, (350g prepared weight), peeled, deseeded and cut into thin discs
Chopped fresh flat-leaf parsley, to garnish

1 Preheat the oven to 200°C, fan 180°C, gas mark 6. Lightly mist a pan with cooking spray and fry the onion over a medium heat for 2-3 minutes until soft.

2 Add the mushrooms, potatoes, fennel and dried herbs, then cook for 5-6 minutes or until just beginning to soften.

3 Add the turkey, then stir in the flour, making sure everything is coated. Stir through the soft cheese, mustard and crème fraîche, then pour in the stock and season to taste. Bring to a boil, then simmer for 12-15 minutes until the sauce has thickened slightly.

4 Pour the turkey mixture into a baking dish and arrange the squash discs in an overlapping layer on top. Mist lightly with cooking spray, then bake for 1 hour until the squash is crisp at the edges. Sprinkle with the parsley, then serve.

SmartPoints values per serving 7
SmartPoints values per recipe 43

DINNER

Roast vegetable & freekeh salad

Freekeh is roasted wheat with a unique nutty flavour and chewy texture. Easy to cook, it's been a staple in Middle Eastern cooking for centuries.

Serves 4 **Prep time** 15 minutes **Cook time** 45 minutes

350g prepared butternut squash cubes
Calorie controlled cooking spray
1 large courgette, thinly sliced
1 aubergine, cut into cubes
1 small fennel bulb, trimmed and thickly sliced
150g button mushrooms, halved
2 teaspoons ground cumin
1 teaspoon smoked paprika
200g freekeh

FOR THE DRESSING
1 tablespoon extra-virgin olive oil
Zest and juice of ½ lemon
2 tablespoons chopped fresh flat-leaf parsley
1 tablespoon chopped fresh mint
½ tablespoon chopped fresh dill

FOR THE SAUCE
1 tablespoon harissa
150g 0% fat natural Greek yogurt

1 Preheat the oven to 180°C, fan 160°C, gas mark 4. Put the squash in a roasting tin. Mist with the cooking spray, season to taste and roast for 15 minutes. Add the other veg to the roasting tin. Mist with the cooking spray, sprinkle over the spices and toss together. Roast for 30 minutes until tender.

2 Meanwhile, cook the freekeh to pack instructions. Drain and set aside in a serving bowl. Make the dressing by whisking together all the ingredients. For the sauce, stir the harissa into the yogurt

3 Toss the roasted veg with the freekeh and half the dressing. Transfer to a platter, drizzle over the remaining dressing and serve with the harissa sauce on the side.

SmartPoints values per serving 7
SmartPoints values per recipe 26

Veggie meatballs & courgetti

Spaghetti and meatballs is an all-time classic – is there anyone who doesn't love it? In this healthy version, even the spaghetti is made of veg!

Serves 4 **Prep time** 25 minutes **Cook time** 1 hour 10 minutes

FOR THE SAUCE
Calorie controlled cooking spray
1 red onion, finely diced
2 garlic cloves, crushed
2 x 400g tins chopped tomatoes
1 tablespoon dried oregano
½ teaspoon dried chilli flakes
1 tablespoon tomato purée
1 teaspoon balsamic vinegar

FOR THE MEATBALLS & COURGETTI
1 red onion, finely diced
1 red pepper, deseeded and finely diced
2 x 410g tins kidney beans, drained and rinsed
50g breadcrumbs made from Weight Watchers Danish Brown bread
1 egg, beaten
1 tablespoon smoked paprika
½ tablespoon dried oregano
4 courgettes, spiralised
Fresh basil, to garnish

1 To make the sauce, mist a pan with cooking spray, add the onion and fry over a medium heat for 6-8 minutes until slightly softened. Add the garlic and cook for 1 minute.

2 Add the tomatoes, oregano, chilli flakes, tomato purée and balsamic vinegar. Season to taste, add a splash of water and simmer for 45 minutes to 1 hour, stirring regularly, and adding more water if it gets too thick.

3 Meanwhile, make the veggie meatballs. Mist a small frying pan with the cooking spray, add the onion and pepper, then fry over a medium heat for 10 minutes, stirring regularly, until softened. Set aside to cool. Blitz the kidney beans with the breadcrumbs, egg, and paprika in a food processor until fairly smooth. Transfer to a bowl and stir through the oregano and the cooled onion and pepper mixture. Season well.

4 Preheat the oven to 200°C, fan 180°C, gas mark 6. Shape the bean mixture into 12 equal balls and place on a lined baking sheet, then bake for 30-40 minutes until crisp and lightly browned.

5 Just before the meatballs are done, put a large frying pan over a high heat and mist with cooking spray. Add the courgetti, then season and cook for 3-4 minutes, stirring, until just softened.

6 Stir the tomato sauce through the courgetti and divide between 4 bowls. Top with 3 veggie meatballs per person and serve garnished with the basil.

SmartPoints values per serving 5
SmartPoints values per recipe 18

Smoked salmon, prawn & dill risotto

Enjoy the delicate flavours of prawns and smoked salmon with the distinctive taste of asparagus in this simple risotto.

Serves 4 **Prep time** 10 minutes **Cook time** 25 minutes

Calorie controlled cooking spray
225g risotto rice
1 small onion, finely chopped
1 garlic clove, finely chopped
100ml dry white wine
850ml hot vegetable stock, made with 1 cube (ensure gluten free)
1 courgette, chopped
100g asparagus, trimmed and chopped
200g smoked salmon, sliced
100g cooked and shelled king prawns
2 tablespoons chopped fresh dill, to garnish

1 Mist a large pan or deep-sided sauté pan with cooking spray. Add the rice, onion and garlic. Stir over a low heat for 1-2 minutes.

2 Pour in the white wine and allow it to bubble up. Add two ladlefuls of hot stock. Stir and cook over a medium heat for 5 minutes, then add the courgette and asparagus. Cook for another 15 minutes, gradually adding the remaining stock a ladleful at a time, until the rice is almost tender.

3 Stir in the salmon, prawns and most of the dill and cook for another 3-4 minutes. Serve, garnished with the remaining dill.

SmartPoints values per serving 9
SmartPoints values per recipe 36

Leek 'cannelloni'

Use hollowed out leeks as a substitute for pasta cannelloni tubes to create this great-tasting veggie meal.

Serves 4 **Prep time** 20 minutes **Cook time** 35 minutes

6 large leeks, trimmed and halved widthways
1 tablespoon olive oil
2 small onions, finely chopped
8 chestnut mushrooms, finely chopped
2 tablespoons chopped fresh flat-leaf parsley
1 tablespoon chopped fresh thyme
180g ricotta
60g fresh white breadcrumbs
60g hard Italian cheese, grated

1 Gently push out the inner core from the leeks (see Cook's tip), leaving 2 layers of leek to make the cannelloni tubes. Finely chop the cores of the leeks and set aside.

2 Bring a large pan of water to the boil, add the leek cannelloni tubes and cook for 5 minutes until just tender. Drain and refresh under cold running water. Drain thoroughly and set aside.

3 Heat the oil in a large frying pan, add the chopped leeks and onions, and cook over a medium heat for 4-5 minutes. Add the mushrooms and fry over a high heat for a further 5 minutes until the leeks are tender. Set aside to cool, then stir in the parsley, thyme and ricotta. Season to taste.

4 Preheat the oven to 200°C, fan 180°C, gas mark 6. Gently spoon the mushroom and leek mixture into the leek tubes and arrange them, side by side, in a small ovenproof dish.

5 Scatter over the breadcrumbs and grated cheese, then bake for 15-20 minutes until crisp and golden.

SmartPoints values per serving 7
SmartPoints values per recipe 27

Ricotta-stuffed chicken

The lovely creamy texture of ricotta makes a deliciously indulgent filling for these tender chicken breasts.

Serves 4 **Prep time** 20 minutes **Cook time** 45 minutes

600g butternut squash, peeled, deseeded and cut into chunks
2 fennel bulbs, trimmed and sliced
2 red onions, sliced
2 garlic cloves, unpeeled
1 tablespoon olive oil
¼ teaspoon dried chilli flakes
4 x 165g skinless chicken breast fillets
200g ricotta
Zest of 1 lemon
4 fresh thyme sprigs, leaves picked
Calorie controlled cooking spray
90ml balsamic vinegar

1 Preheat the oven to 200°C, fan 180°C, gas mark 6. Put the squash, fennel, onions and garlic in a roasting tin. Drizzle over the oil and sprinkle over the chilli flakes. Season well and roast for 40 minutes until golden and tender.

2 Meanwhile, put the chicken between two sheets of cling film and flatten with a rolling pin to a thickness of 5mm. Mix the ricotta with the lemon zest and thyme leaves. Season well, and spread over the chicken. Roll tightly into sausage shapes.

3 Mist a large nonstick frying pan with cooking spray and place over a medium-high heat. Add the chicken and cook until just golden. Transfer to a roasting tin lined with a double length of foil. Fold the foil to create a parcel and bake for 25 minutes.

4 Meanwhile, bring the vinegar to the boil in a small pan. Cook for 2-3 minutes until syrupy, then remove from the heat. When the veg is cooked, remove from the oven. Squeeze the roasted garlic flesh from the skins and toss through the veg with the balsamic syrup. Cut the chicken into slices and serve with the vegetables.

SmartPoints values per serving 7
SmartPoints values per recipe 27

3 easy turkey ragù ideas

This is a great batch-cook recipe to freeze for later. Serve it with spaghetti, or turn it into other delicious dinners – turn the page for more recipes.

Easy turkey ragù

Serves 4 **Prep time** 10 minutes **Cook time** 35 minutes  

Mist a large saucepan with **calorie controlled cooking spray**, then cook 1 chopped **onion**, 1 large peeled and cubed **carrot** and a stick of chopped **celery** for 8-10 minutes over a medium heat until golden brown. Add a crushed **garlic clove** and cook for another minute, then add 1 teaspoon **dried mixed herbs** and 500g **2% fat turkey breast mince**, and cook for 4-5 minutes. Stir in 1 tablespoon **balsamic vinegar** and 2 x 390g cartons **chopped tomatoes**. Half-fill one of the tomato cartons with water, and add to the pan. Simmer for 12-14 minutes until the sauce has thickened.

SmartPoints values per serving 2
SmartPoints values per recipe 7

Flavour boosters

Add flavour to the basic ragu with:

- **Fresh thyme leaves**
- **Lemon zest**
- **Fennel seeds**

Nachos

Serves 4 **Prep time** 10 minutes **Cook time** 12 minutes GF

Deseed and thinly slice 1 **red chilli**, then add it to half a batch of the basic **turkey ragù**. Stir in 150g **roasted red peppers** in brine that have been drained and roughly chopped. Meanwhile, preheat the oven to 180°C, fan 160°C, gas mark 4. Arrange 100g **tortilla chips** (ensure gluten free) in a baking dish, and top them with the ragù. Sprinkle over 50g grated **half-fat Cheddar cheese** and bake for 10-12 minutes until the cheese is golden and bubbling. Serve topped with 1 tablespoon **reduced-fat soured cream** per serving and sliced **spring onions**.

8 SmartPoints value

SmartPoints values per serving 8
SmartPoints values per recipe 30

Chilli con carne    

Serves 4 **Prep time** 5 minutes
Cook time 25 minutes

To 1 batch of the basic **turkey ragù**, add 1 teaspoon hot **chilli powder**, a 400g tin drained and rinsed **kidney beans**, and 2 deseeded and sliced **red peppers**, and cook for 5 minutes to heat through. Cook 250g **brown rice** according to pack instructions and divide among 4 bowls. Spoon the chilli on top, then add 1 tablespoon **low-fat natural yogurt** and a sprinkling of chopped **fresh coriander** leaves to each bowl, then serve.

SmartPoints values per serving 10
SmartPoints values per recipe 41

Sloppy Joe pizza

Serves 4 **Prep time** 20 minutes
Cook time 16-18 minutes V

To 1 batch of the basic **turkey ragù**, add 2 teaspoons mild **chilli powder** and 1 teaspoon **mustard powder**. Put 150g **strong white flour** and 150g **strong wholemeal flour** in a bowl and add 7g **fast-action dried yeast**. Pour in 250ml lukewarm water and mix for 1-2 minutes to a soft dough. Turn out onto a lightly floured surface and divide into two, then roll each half out into a 22-24cm circle. Put each base onto a baking tray that's been misted with **calorie controlled cooking spray**. Preheat the oven to 220°C, fan 200°C, gas mark 7. Top the pizza bases with the ragù sauce, then scatter over 125g torn **light mozzarella**. Bake for 16-18 minutes, until the cheese is golden and the base is crisp. Sprinkle with chopped **fresh parsley**, cut into slices and serve with **salad leaves**.

SmartPoints values per serving 7
SmartPoints values per recipe 28

Snacks & Puds

Prawn summer rolls

These no-cook spring rolls are a favourite street food in Vietnam and are full of fresh Asian flavours.

Makes 12 **Prep time** 30 minutes

FOR THE ROLLS
12 rice paper wrappers
300g cooked king prawns
1 carrot, julienned
1 red pepper, deseeded and cut into thin strips
1 yellow pepper, deseeded and cut into thin strips
¼ Chinese cabbage, shredded
Handful of fresh coriander, leaves picked
Handful of fresh mint, roughly chopped
Handful of fresh Thai basil, roughly chopped

FOR THE DIPPING SAUCE
3 tablespoons soy sauce (ensure gluten free)
2 tablespoons rice wine vinegar
1 tablespoon sriracha hot chilli sauce
2 spring onions, finely sliced

1 Put one of the rice paper wrappers in a bowl of hot water and leave for 8-10 seconds until soft. Carefully remove from the water and lay on a board, unfolding into a circle. Lay three prawns in the middle of the wrapper, add a small handful of the carrots, pepper and cabbage, then scatter over a few of the fresh herbs.

2 Roll up into a cigar shape, folding over the edges and tucking inside to secure. Repeat until you have used all of the wrappers.

3 To make the dipping sauce, mix together the soy, rice wine vinegar and sriracha sauce. Scatter over the spring onions. Serve the rolls with the dipping sauce on the side.

SmartPoints value per roll 2
SmartPoints values per recipe 25

INSIDE INFO

Thai basil has a slightly minty, citrussy flavour. If you can't find it, use regular basil instead.

Celeriac crisps with tomato salsa

These healthy celeriac crisps are the perfect substitute for tortilla chips – dunk them in tangy salsa and enjoy the crunch.

Serves 4 **Prep time** 20 minutes **Cook time** 25 minutes

350g celeriac
Calorie controlled cooking spray
3 tomatoes
½ red onion, diced
Handful of chopped coriander
1 tablespoon olive oil
Juice of 1 lime

1 Preheat the oven to 220°C, fan 200°C, gas mark 7. Peel and finely slice the celeriac and put on two baking trays, making sure that the slices don't overlap. Mist with cooking spray and season to taste.

2 Bake for 20 minutes until browned and crisp, then transfer to a large dish, making sure to keep the slices apart to prevent them going soggy.

3 Meanwhile, put the tomatoes in a heatproof dish and cover with boiling water. Let them sit for 30 seconds, then drain and run under cold water to loosen the skin. Peel the tomatoes, then quarter, deseed and finely dice them.

4 Put the tomato in a bowl with the onion, coriander, olive oil and lime juice. Season to taste and serve with the crisps.

SmartPoints value per serving 1
SmartPoints values per recipe 5

Why not try baking other root veg such as parsnip, sweet potato and carrot. See p180 for details.

Courgette & harissa mini muffins

These savoury muffins make a delicious change from sweet ones. Try them with your afternoon cuppa, or make a batch for a weekend picnic.

Makes 12 **Prep time** 15 **Cook time** 25 minutes

100g plain flour
1 teaspoon baking powder
25g parmesan, grated
75g low-fat spread
75g 0% fat natural Greek yogurt
1 egg
1 courgette, grated
1 teaspoon harissa
Handful of fresh dill, chopped
Calorie controlled cooking spray

1 Preheat the oven to 200°C, fan 180°C, gas mark 6. Mix the plain flour, baking powder and grated parmesan together in a large mixing bowl.

2 Melt the low-fat spread in a pan over a gentle heat, then leave to cool slightly. Whisk together the yogurt and egg in a jug, then add the melted spread. Add the courgette, harissa and dill, then season and mix well to combine.

3 Add the wet ingredients to the dry ingredients in the mixing bowl and stir to combine. Mist a 12-hole mini muffin tin with calorie controlled spray, then divide the mixture between the holes. Bake in the oven for 15-20 minutes, or until a skewer inserted in the centre of a muffin comes out clean.

4 Leave to cool in the tin for 10 minutes, then transfer to a wire rack. Serve warm or cold.

SmartPoints value per muffin 2
SmartPoints values per recipe 27

Pea & mint dip with Melba toasts

Minted peas are puréed with quark and yogurt to make this fresh-tasting dip, which goes perfectly with crisp, thin toasts.

Serves 2 **Prep time** 10 minutes **Cook time** 10 minutes

2 Warburtons Brown Sandwich Thins, split in half
Calorie controlled cooking spray
1 teaspoon za'atar
125g cooked peas
Handful of fresh mint
30g quark
30g 0% fat natural Greek yogurt

1 Preheat the oven to 200°C, fan 180°C, gas mark 6. Flatten the sandwich thin halves with a rolling pin. Cut into triangles, put on a baking tray and mist with the cooking spray.

2 Sprinkle over the za'atar and bake for 6-8 minutes until crisp. Meanwhile, blitz the peas with the mint, quark and yogurt. Serve with the toast triangles.

SmartPoints value per serving 5
SmartPoints values per recipe 9

Filo sausage rolls

Love sausage rolls? These ones use crisp filo pastry instead of puff, making them the smarter option, but every bit as good.

Makes 12 **Prep time** 15 minutes **Cook time** 30 minutes

Calorie controlled cooking spray
2 shallots, finely chopped
8 reduced-fat pork sausages
1 tablespoon butter
3 sheets filo pastry
1 egg, beaten
1 teaspoon fennel seeds

1 Preheat the oven to 200°C, fan 180°C, gas mark 6 and line a baking sheet with baking paper. Mist a frying pan with cooking spray and cook the shallots over a medium heat for 3-4 minutes until soft.

2 Remove the skin from the sausages and mix the meat with the cooked shallots in a bowl. Melt the butter in a small pan over a low heat.

3 Lay one of the filo pastry sheets on a board and dot with some of the melted butter. Lay a second sheet of filo on top of the first, dot with more melted butter then repeat with the third sheet. Trim the edges, then cut in half to make two rectangular strips.

4 Put half the sausage mixture down the centre of each pastry strip, then brush the edges of the pastry with the remaining melted butter. Roll up the pastry to enclose the sausage meat and slice into 4cm pieces.

5 Put the sausage rolls on the baking sheet, brush with the beaten egg and sprinkle over the fennel seeds, then bake in the oven for 20-25 minutes until golden and cooked through.

SmartPoints value per roll 3
SmartPoints values per recipe 33

Root veg crisps with houmous

These crunchy baked vegetable crisps go perfectly with this freshly made houmous that tastes better than any store-bought version.

Serves 6 **Prep time** 15 minutes **Cook time** 1 hour

1 carrot
1 parsnip
1 sweet potato
1 fresh beetroot
1 tablespoon vegetable oil
1 teaspoon smoked paprika

FOR THE HOUMOUS
400g tin chickpeas
150g roasted red peppers from a jar (in water), drained
1 red chilli, deseeded and finely chopped
½ teaspoon cayenne pepper
1 tablespoon tahini
1 large garlic clove, peeled and bruised with the back of a knife
Juice of ½ lemon

1 Make the crisps. Preheat the oven to 180°C, fan 160°C, gas mark 4. Trim the veg, then slice very thinly using a knife or a mandoline. Pat dry with kitchen paper, then put in a bowl with the oil and paprika. Mix everything together until evenly coated.

2 Lay the crisps on two lined baking trays (you will need to do this in batches) and bake for 16-18 minutes, or until crisp and golden. Some of the veg will cook quicker than others, depending on size, so keep an eye on them and remove them as they're done. Season and leave to cool on a wire rack.

3 Meanwhile, for the houmous, drain the chickpeas and reserve the liquid. Blitz the chickpeas with the remaining ingredients in a food processor – if the mixture is too thick, you can loosen it with a little of the reserved water. Season to taste.

4 Serve the houmous with the crisps for dipping.

Try serving this with some fresh veggie crudités, such as asparagus tips, carrot and cucumber.

SmartPoints value per serving 5
SmartPoints values per recipe 32

Linzi's perfect popcorn

Popcorn is a ridiculously easy snack – you can keep the kernels in your storecupboard and make it when you feel like it. But don't just stick with boring old plain – add bags of flavour with scrummy seasonings.

'Popcorn is my go-to snack – I never get tired of it! To do it in the microwave, just put it in a microwave-proof bowl and cover with a vented lid. Microwave on high for 3-4 minutes, until there's about 5 seconds between pops. Be careful when you take off the lid as it'll be steaming hot!'
Linzi

STEP 1: get popping

Pop 80g popcorn kernels in an air popper or microwave – this is enough for 4 servings, at 2 SmartPoints per serving. Mist the popcorn with calorie controlled cooking spray to help the flavourings stick. Add the SmartPoints for the toppings to the popcorn.

STEP 2: sprinkle over the flavouring

Clockwise from top left:

Kale & lemon

(0 SmartPoints per serving)
Spread 4 handfuls of chopped kale on a tray, mist with calorie controlled cooking spray and sprinkle over ½ teaspoon salt. Bake at 160°C, fan 140°C, gas mark 3 for 10 minutes until crispy. Whizz in a blender with 2 teaspoons grated lemon zest.

Salt & vinegar

(1 SmartPoint per serving)
Sprinkle popcorn with ½ teaspoon salt, then drizzle over 2 tablespoons balsamic vinegar.

Herb & garlic

(0 SmartPoints per serving)
Chop a small handful each of fresh chives and fresh parsley, then mix with 1 teaspoon chopped fresh rosemary, the grated zest of 1 lemon and ½ teaspoon garlic salt.

Tex-Mex

(0 SmartPoints per serving)
Mix 1 teaspoon chilli, 1 teaspoon ground cumin, 1 teaspoon smoked paprika, ½ teaspoon garlic powder and ½ teaspoon salt.

Seaweed & sesame

(1 SmartPoint per serving)
Crumble 3 sheets nori seaweed, and mix with 1 tablespoon toasted sesame seeds and ½ teaspoon salt.

Sugar & spice

(1 SmartPoint per serving)
Mix 2 tablespoons icing sugar with 1 teaspoon ground cinnamon, ¼ teaspoon freshly grated nutmeg, ¼ teaspoon ground allspice and ¼ teaspoon salt.

Sweet potato & coconut scones

Try these deliciously moist scones for a teatime treat – the sweet potato adds a touch of sweetness and colour.

Makes 14 **Prep time** 10 minutes **Cook time** 1 hour 15 minutes

2 sweet potatoes (about 600g)
2 tablespoons clear honey
1 egg, lightly beaten
350g self-raising flour, plus extra for dusting
1 teaspoon baking powder
50g low-fat spread
50ml reduced-fat coconut milk, plus extra for brushing
20g desiccated coconut

1 Preheat the oven to 200°C, fan 180°C, gas mark 6. Line 2 baking trays with baking paper. Put the sweet potatoes in a roasting tin and bake for 1 hour until tender. Set aside to cool.

2 When cool enough to handle, scoop out the flesh (you'll need 250g), mash with the honey and egg, and then set aside in a bowl.

3 Meanwhile, sift the flour and baking powder into a large bowl. Rub in the spread, then mix in the sweet potato mixture, coconut milk and coconut.

4 Use your hands to form the mixture into a dough then tip onto a floured surface. Knead briefly and roll out to a 1.5cm thickness. Use a 6.5cm cutter to stamp out 14 scones – you'll need to re-roll the trimmings.

5 Transfer the scones to the prepared trays, then brush with a little coconut milk. Bake for 15-18 minutes until risen and golden.

SmartPoints value per scone 6
SmartPoints values per recipe 80

TRY THIS

Serve with fresh mango and passion fruit, and 1 tablespoon of 0% fat natural Greek yogurt for 1 extra SmartPoint.

Spiced date buns

Who could resist one of these spicy fruit scrolls – the perfect accompaniment to an afternoon cuppa.

Makes 14 **Prep time** 20 minutes, plus proving **Cook time** 40 minutes

325ml semi-skimmed milk
3 tablespoons clear honey
300g plain flour, plus extra for dusting
150g wholemeal flour
7g sachet fast-action dried yeast
¾ teaspoon ground cinnamon
50g baking block, melted
Calorie controlled cooking spray
2 tablespoons freshly squeezed orange juice

FOR THE DATE FILLING
75g medjool dates, pitted
⅛ teaspoon rosewater
1 teaspoon orange zest
3 cardamom pods, seeds only, crushed
2 pinches of salt

1 Put the milk and 1 tablespoon honey in a pan and heat gently, stirring, until warm. Remove from the heat.

2 In the bowl of a freestanding mixer, combine both flours, the yeast, ½ teaspoon of the cinnamon and a pinch of salt. Add the warm milk mixture and melted baking block.

3 Using the dough-hook, mix on low speed until the dough comes together. Increase to medium-high and mix for 3 minutes. Put in a bowl that's been misted with cooking spray. Cover with cling film and leave in a warm place until doubled in size – about 1 hour.

4 Meanwhile, make the filling. Bring the dates, a large pinch of salt and 125ml water to a boil in a small pan. Reduce the heat and simmer until the dates are mushy and the water has almost evaporated. Cool slightly, then stir in the remaining filling ingredients.

5 Line a 24cm x 26cm baking tin with baking paper. Knock back the dough, dust with a little flour and transfer to a lightly floured surface. Roll out to a rectangle about 30cm x 45cm and 5mm thick. Spread the date mixture over the top. Roll up from the long side into a log shape. Cut into 14 equal pieces, then put them in the baking tin, cut-side up. Cover with cling film and leave in a warm place for 45 minutes to rise.

6 Preheat the oven to 220°C, fan 200°C, gas mark 7. Bake the buns for 25-28 minutes until risen and golden.

7 Make a glaze by putting the remaining 2 tablespoons of honey, orange juice and remaining cinnamon in a pan with 50ml water. Bring to a boil, bubble for 2 minutes, then simmer for 3 minutes, until thickened. Brush the buns with the glaze while still warm, then allow to cool before serving.

SmartPoints value per bun 6
SmartPoints values per recipe 88

Raspberry & white chocolate muffins

The yogurt in these yummy muffins helps keep them soft, while the mixed spice gives them a distinctive flavour.

Makes 16 **Prep time** 15 minutes **Cook time** 20-25 minutes

3 tablespoons low-fat spread
150g caster sugar
2 eggs
150g 0% fat natural Greek yogurt
200g plain flour, sifted
1 teaspoon bicarbonate of soda
1 teaspoon mixed spice
1 teaspoon vanilla extract
50g white chocolate chips
100g raspberries, chopped
1 tablespoon icing sugar, to decorate

1 Preheat the oven to 180°C, fan 160°C, gas mark 4. Line 2 x 8-hole muffin tins with paper cupcake or muffin cases.

2 With a hand-held electric mixer, beat the spread and sugar until fluffy. Beat in the eggs and yogurt, then the flour, bicarbonate of soda, mixed spice and vanilla extract. Fold in the chocolate and chopped raspberries.

3 Divide the batter between the cases, then bake for 20-25 minutes until risen and golden, and a skewer inserted in the middle comes out clean. Cool the muffins on a cooling rack, then dust with icing sugar to serve.

SmartPoints value per muffin 5
SmartPoints values per recipe 85

Chocolate chunk oatmeal cookies

Soft and chewy with little explosions of dark chocolate. These oaty treats are perfect for when you fancy something sweet.

Makes 16 **Prep time** 10-15 minutes
Cook time 10-12 minutes, plus cooling

45g unsalted butter
75g light muscovado sugar
50g plain flour
½ teaspoon baking powder
70g porridge oats
1 egg, lightly beaten
½ teaspoon vanilla extract
50g dark chocolate, roughly chopped
Pinch of salt

1 Preheat the oven to 180°C, fan 160°C, gas mark 4. Line 2 baking sheets with greaseproof paper. Put the butter in a small pan and melt over a low heat. Add the sugar, and stir until dissolved.

2 Combine the flour, baking powder and oats in a bowl with a pinch of salt, then add the butter and sugar mixture, egg and vanilla extract. Fold in the chopped chocolate.

3 Roll the mixture into 16 evenly sized balls and put them on the baking sheets, leaving plenty of space between them. Bake for 10-12 minutes or until golden, then cool on a wire rack.

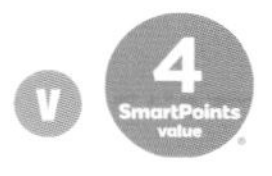

SmartPoints value per cookie 4
SmartPoints values per recipe 64

NE AUSTEN • PERSUASION
VINTAGE CLASSICS

Cinnamon ice cream with warm apples

Warm apples and our wonderful low SmartPoints ice cream made from ripe bananas are *the* perfect, guilt-free way to get your sweet fix.

Serves 4 **Prep time** 35 minutes, plus freezing
Cook time 10-15 minutes

4 ripe medium bananas, unpeeled
2 teaspoons ground cinnamon

FOR THE APPLES
4 apples, unpeeled
1 teaspoon light brown sugar

FOR THE CIGARILLOS
45g sheet filo pastry
Calorie controlled cooking spray
½ teaspoon icing sugar

1 For the ice cream, freeze the bananas in their skins for at least 6 hours. Take them out of the freezer and leave to stand for 10 minutes. Peel and roughly chop, then put in a food processor and pulse a few times until smooth. Stir in the cinnamon, transfer to a shallow dish and put in the freezer.

2 To make the cigarillos, preheat the oven to 200°C, fan 180°C, gas mark 6. Using a sharp knife, cut the filo into 8 rough squares. Starting at one corner, roll each square up tightly to form a cigarillo.

3 Mist with cooking spray and sprinkle with the icing sugar. Bake for 10 minutes until crisp and golden.

4 Meanwhile, to prepare the apples, quarter and core them, then cut into wedges. Heat gently in a pan with the sugar (no water) for 10-15 minutes, or until just soft.

5 Serve the apples with the ice cream and cigarillos.

COOK'S TIP

For a No Count dessert, serve the ice cream on it's own or with sliced fresh fruit.

SmartPoints value per serving 1
SmartPoints values per recipe 5

SNACKS & PUDS

Courgette cake with lemon & poppy seed frosting

Grated courgettes give this lush cake a lovely moist texture and flavour, which is perfectly complemented by a zingy citrus icing.

Serves 12 **Prep time** 10 minutes **Cook time** 40 minutes

200g courgettes
150g golden caster sugar
150g low-fat spread
3 eggs, beaten
150g self-raising flour
1 teaspoon bicarbonate of soda

FOR THE FROSTING
25g icing sugar
75g low-fat soft cheese
Zest of ½ lemon, plus
2 teaspoons of juice
1 teaspoon poppy seeds

1 Preheat the oven to 180°C, fan 160°C, gas mark 4 and line the base of a 20cm round loose-bottomed cake tin with baking paper. Coarsely grate the courgettes and squeeze out any excess liquid with your hands, then set aside.

2 Beat together the sugar and spread with an electric whisk until pale and creamy. Gradually add the eggs. Fold in the flour and bicarbonate of soda, then gently stir in the grated courgette. Spoon into the prepared tin and level off the top.

3 Bake for 40 minutes until the cake is golden and springs back when lightly touched. Cool for 10 minutes in the tin, then turn out onto a wire rack to cool. Beat together the icing sugar, soft cheese, lemon juice and poppy seeds, then spread over the top of the cake and sprinkle over the lemon zest. Slice and serve.

SmartPoints value per serving 7
SmartPoints values per recipe 85

GREAT IDEA

This recipe can be used to make 12 cupcakes – use paper cases in a muffin tin and bake for 20-25 minutes.

No bake oaty fruit bites

Ditch the chocolate and crisps for these delicious snacks – the perfect sweet treat to have when you're on the go.

Makes 12 **Prep time** 10 minutes, plus 30 minutes chilling time

75g rolled oats
35g desiccated coconut
25g dried cranberries, finely chopped
45g roasted hazelnuts, chopped
60g smooth peanut butter
75g clear honey
½ teaspoon vanilla extract

1 Combine the rolled oats, desiccated coconut, dried cranberries and chopped hazelnuts in a bowl.

2 Add the peanut butter, honey and vanilla extract, then mix well to combine. The mixture should be quite sticky.

3 Chill for 30 minutes, then form into 12 balls. Keep them in the fridge until you're ready to eat them.

SmartPoints value per bite 5
SmartPoints values per recipe 59

TRY THIS

Spice these up, if you like, by adding ½ teaspoon ground cinnamon or ginger with the dry ingredients.

Apple rose tarts

Our elegant rose-inspired desserts definitely have the wow factor – and they taste as good as they look!

Makes 10 **Prep time** 30 minutes **Cook time** 25-30 minutes

2 pink lady apples
2 tablespoons freshly squeezed lemon juice
¼ teaspoon ground cinnamon
1 sheet lighter puff pastry
2 tablespoons apricot jam
Calorie controlled cooking spray
½ teaspoon icing sugar

1 Preheat the oven to 200°C, fan 180°C, gas mark 6. Cut the apples in half from top to bottom. Core, then slice thinly across the width. Half-fill a medium bowl with water; add the lemon juice and apples. Microwave on high for 2 minutes. Drain, then sprinkle in the cinnamon and gently turn the apples to coat.

2 Unroll the pastry and use a rolling pin to further roll it out to 50cm long. Cut widthways into 10 equal strips. Mix the jam with 2 tablespoons of water and brush down the centre of each strip. Put 8 apple slices along the top half of each strip, slightly overlapping, with the peel at the top. Fold the bottom half of the pastry up and over the apple slices, leaving the tops visible.

3 Tightly roll up the pastry strips so the apples peek out of the top. Place in a muffin tin misted with cooking spray.

4 Bake for 20-25 minutes. Allow to cool, then dust with the icing sugar to serve.

SmartPoints value per tart 5
SmartPoints values per recipe 49

INSIDE INFO

As well as adding to the flavour, the lemon juice in the recipe also helps stop the apples from turning brown.

Chocolate loaf with coffee glaze

Chocolate and coffee are always a wicked combination – and the agave nectar gives this cake a subtle sweetness.

Serves 12 **Prep time** 20 minutes **Cook time** 45-50 minutes

125g low-fat spread, plus extra for greasing
160g dark agave nectar
2 eggs
1 teaspoon vanilla bean paste
225g plain flour
30g cocoa powder
1 teaspoon baking powder
¼ teaspoon bicarbonate of soda
1 tablespoon semi-skimmed milk

FOR THE GLAZE
2 tablespoons cocoa powder
2 tablespoons dark agave nectar
1 tablespoon strong brewed coffee

1 Preheat the oven to 180°C, fan 160°C, gas mark 4. Grease a 900g loaf tin and line with baking paper.

2 Beat the low-fat spread and agave nectar together in a large bowl until well combined. Beat in the eggs one at a time, then stir in the vanilla bean paste.

3 Sift the flour, cocoa powder, baking powder and bicarbonate of soda into the bowl, then fold into the egg mixture. Fold in the milk.

4 Spoon the batter into the prepared tin and bake for 45-50 minutes, or until a skewer inserted into the centre of the cake comes out clean. Leave to cool in the tin for 10-15 minutes, then turn out onto a cooling rack to cool completely.

5 To make the glaze, mix the cocoa powder and agave nectar together so you have a smooth paste. Stir in the coffee. Drizzle the glaze over the cold cake.

SmartPoints value per serving 7
SmartPoints values per recipe 84

Lemon & ginger frozen yogurt

This is a delicious alternative to ice-cream that makes a great summer dessert. Serve it with fresh fruit or in ice cream cones.

Serves 4 **Prep time** 5 minutes, plus churning and freezing

Grated zest and juice of 3 lemons
50g stem ginger, chopped
2 tablespoons agave nectar
500g 0% fat natural Greek yogurt

1 Put the lemon zest, juice, stem ginger and agave nectar in a pan and bring to a simmer. Simmer gently for 2-3 minutes until the syrup is slightly reduced. Remove from the heat and leave to cool, then chill until completely cold.

2 Stir the syrup through the yogurt, then transfer to an ice cream machine and churn to your manufacturer's recommendations. Transfer to an airtight container and freeze until required.

3 If you don't have an ice cream machine, you can pour the mixture straight into an airtight container and place in the freezer. Freeze for around 3 hours, removing every hour to stir the yogurt. This will break up the ice crystals and help it to freeze smoothly.

4 Remove from the freezer for 10 minutes before serving.

SmartPoints value per serving 5
SmartPoints values per recipe 20

Poached fruit

Gently simmering fruit with spices creates a simple but delicious dessert. Make a double batch to freeze and use later in other recipes.

Basic poached fruit

Serves 4 **Prep time** 15 minutes
Cook time 25 minutes V GF *

Put 200ml **apple juice**, 1 **cinnamon stick** and 1 **star anise** in a saucepan and heat gently until it starts to simmer. Add 2 **apples** and 3 **pears** that have been peeled, cored and cut into chunky wedges. Remove the stones from 4 **plums** and cut the fruit into quarters, then add these to the pan, along with 4 quartered **figs**. Simmer for around 20 minutes until the fruit is tender, adding 150g **blackberries** for the last 5 minutes. Remove the fruit from the pan with a slotted spoon and set aside. Continue cooking the liquid until it reduces to a sticky syrup. Remove the cinnamon and star anise, then pour the syrup over the fruit. Serve warm, or cool and use in other recipes.

1 SmartPoints value

SmartPoints values per serving 1
SmartPoints values per recipe 5

Flavour boosters

Try other spices and flavourings to complement the fruit you're using. Ground ginger, grated orange zest or freshly grated nutmeg work well.

Fruit crumble

Serves 4 Prep time 10 minutes
Cook time 25 minutes V GF

Preheat the oven to 200°C, fan 180°C, gas mark 6. Mix 30g **porridge oats**, 60g **plain flour**, 20g **brown sugar** and 1 teaspoon **cinnamon** together in a bowl. Rub in 50g **low-fat spread** using your finger tips, until the mixture resembles coarse breadcrumbs. Put the **poached fruit** into a 20cm x 22cm dish. Scatter over the crumble and bake for 20-25 minutes, until golden brown. Serve with 1 tablespoon **0% fat natural Greek yogurt** per serving.

8 SmartPoints value

SmartPoints values per serving 8
SmartPoints values per recipe 28

Easy trifle

Serves 8 **Prep time** 10 minutes, plus chilling V GF

Line the base of a glass serving bowl with 100g **sponge finger biscuits**. Spoon over the **poached fruit**, levelling it so you have an even layer. Scatter over 30g crumbled **Amaretti biscuits**, then pour over 75ml **port**. Spoon over 250g **low-fat ready made custard** and chill in the fridge for a couple of hours. Stir 25g chopped **stem ginger** through 350g **0% fat natural Greek yogurt**. Spoon the yogurt over the custard layer. Keep refrigerated until you're ready to serve.

SmartPoints values per serving 6
SmartPoints values per recipe 51

'Mix things up a bit and use different fruits – peaches, apricots and nectarines are all great, but you can also poach mangos and kiwifruit, too. Just make sure you start with fruit that's still firm and not overripe!' *Lina*

Poached fruit pavlova

Serves 12 **Prep time** 20 minutes, plus cooling **Cook time** 1 hour V GF

Preheat the oven to 150°C, fan 130°C, gas mark 2. Put 4 **egg whites** in the bowl of a freestanding mixer. Whisk until the egg whites form soft peaks, then gradually add 200g **caster sugar**, a tablespoon at a time. When the meringue looks nice and glossy, add 1 teaspoon **vinegar** and 1 teaspoon **cornflour**, and whisk for another 1 minute to combine. Line a baking sheet with baking paper and spoon on the meringue, shaping it into a circle the size of small dinner plate. Use a spoon to create a large indent in the middle. Bake in the oven for an hour, then turn off the oven and leave the meringue inside until completely cool. Top the pavlova with 500g 0% fat natural **Greek yogurt**, and spoon over 1 whole batch of the **poached fruit**.

SmartPoints value per serving 5
SmartPoints values per recipe 61

H. CHEN

Meal plans

PERSUASION
VINTAGE CLASSICS

Family meal plan

These meal ideas include some classic family dishes and they'll fit perfectly into your daily SmartPoints allowance.

MONDAY

Breakfast (4 SmartPoints value)
Muesli muffins, p56

Lunch (7 SmartPoints value)
Pancakes with leek & ham, p100

Dinner (6 SmartPoints value)
Aubergine lasagne, p128

17 SmartPoints

TUESDAY

Breakfast (4 SmartPoints value)
Ham & egg toast (without spread), p44

Lunch (4 SmartPoints value)
Butternut squash falafels, p106

Dinner (13 SmartPoints value)
Fish pie, p144

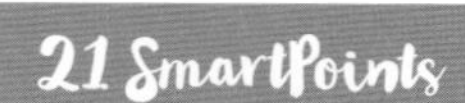

WEDNESDAY

Breakfast (7 SmartPoints value)
Coconut pancakes with tropical fruit, p48

Lunch

Minestrone soup, p62

Dinner (11 SmartPoints value)
Turkey burger with wedges, p126

20 SmartPoints

Breakfast

Muesli muffins, p56

Lunch

9 SmartPoints value

Courgette & feta fritters, p96

Dinner

Chicken filo pie, p110

23 SmartPoints

FRIDAY

Breakfast

4 SmartPoints value

Ham & egg toast (without spread), p44

Lunch

7 SmartPoints value

Chicken satay noodle salad, p74

Dinner

8 SmartPoints value

Crumbed cod with potato salad, p150

19 SmartPoints

LITTLE EXTRAS

Snack

4 SmartPoints value

Chocolate chunk oatmeal cookies p190

Dessert

Fruit crumble, p205

Meal plan notes

- Use any spare SmartPoints from your daily allowance on snacks, puddings or drinks.
- Repeat your favourite days on the weekends.
- Muffins and cookies will keep for up to a week in an airtight container.

Serves 1 meal plan

All these recipes can be made to serve 1, or portioned and frozen for later.

MONDAY

Breakfast 5 SmartPoints value
Bacon & avocado toast (without spread), p44

Lunch 9 SmartPoints value
Chicken & avocado wrap, p70

Dinner 8 SmartPoints value
Chicken & mushroom masala (½ recipe), p114

22 SmartPoints

TUESDAY

Breakfast 7 SmartPoints value
Oat & banana smoothie (½ recipe), p40

Lunch 10 SmartPoints value
Asparagus & salmon wrap, p78

Dinner 7 SmartPoints value
Bacon & cabbage pasta (¼ recipe), p146

24 SmartPoints

WEDNESDAY

Breakfast 3 SmartPoints value
Salmon & cucumber toast (without spread), p44

Lunch 6 SmartPoints value
Chicken tikka naan (½ recipe), p64

Dinner 13 SmartPoints value
Fish pie, p144 (freeze leftovers for later)

22 SmartPoints

THURSDAY

Breakfast — 7 SmartPoints value
Oat & banana smoothie (½ recipe), p40

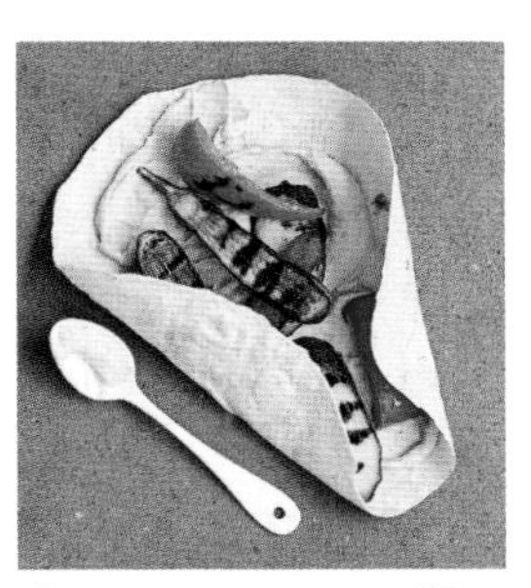

Lunch — 6 SmartPoints value
Houmous & griddled veg wrap, p78

Dinner — 11 SmartPoints value
Turkey burger with wedges, p126

24 SmartPoints

FRIDAY

Breakfast — 9 SmartPoints value
Smoked salmon bagels (½ recipe), p42

Lunch — 4 SmartPoints value
Butternut squash falafels, p106

Dinner — 11 SmartPoints value
Cottage pie, p130 (freeze leftovers for later)

24 SmartPoints

LITTLE EXTRAS

Snack — 5 SmartPoints value
Pea & mint dip (½ recipe), p176

Dessert — 5 SmartPoints value
Lemon & ginger frozen yogurt, p202

Meal plan notes

- Use any spare SmartPoints from your daily allowance on snacks, puddings or drinks.
- Make half the recipe, or portion and freeze leftovers for later where indicated
- Repeat your favourite days on the weekends.

Serves 2 meal plan

Losing weight together? This meal plan is perfect for couples.

MONDAY

Breakfast 6 SmartPoints value
Turkey, egg & avocado breakfast, p34

Lunch 10 SmartPoints value
Mozzarella & tomato panzanella, p60

Dinner 7 SmartPoints value
Chilli & tomato tagliatelle (½ recipe), p124

23 SmartPoints

TUESDAY

Breakfast 9 SmartPoints value
Mini bagels with smoked salmon, p42

Lunch 5 SmartPoints value
Tuna & bean salad, p88

Dinner 7 SmartPoints value
Ricotta-stuffed chicken (½ recipe), p162

21 SmartPoints

WEDNESDAY

Breakfast 7 SmartPoints value
Oat & banana smoothie, p40

Lunch 6 SmartPoints value
Chicken tikka naan, p64

Dinner 13 SmartPoints value
Fish pie (freeze ½ for later), p144

26 SmartPoints

Breakfast

Oat & banana smoothie, p40

Lunch

Beef pitta pockets, p72

Dinner 5 SmartPoints value

Stuffed aubergines (½ recipe), p148

23 SmartPoints

FRIDAY

Breakfast 7 SmartPoints value

Porridge with spiced apple, p46

Lunch

Fish tacos, p92

Dinner 8 SmartPoints value

Chicken & mushroom masala, p114

22 SmartPoints

LITTLE EXTRAS

Snack 2 SmartPoints value

Courgette mini muffins, p174

Dessert 1 SmartPoints value

Cinnamon ice cream (½ recipe), p192

Meal plan notes

- Use any spare SmartPoints from your daily allowance on snacks, puddings or drinks.
- Make half the recipe, or portion and freeze leftovers for later where indicated
- Repeat your favourite days on the weekends.

Quick meal plan

Busy week ahead? These super-speedy meals are on the table in a flash.

MONDAY

Breakfast 6 SmartPoints value
Basic muesli, p54

Lunch 9 SmartPoints value
Warm chicken & pancetta salad, p68

Dinner 8 SmartPoints value

Bibimbap, p122

23 SmartPoints

TUESDAY

Breakfast 3 SmartPoints value
Ricotta & peach toast, p44

Lunch 11 SmartPoints value
Beef pitta pockets, p72

Dinner 10 SmartPoints value
Tikka-spiced salmon with pilaf, p112

24 SmartPoints

WEDNESDAY

Breakfast 7 SmartPoints value
Oat & banana smoothie, p40

Lunch 7 SmartPoints value
Fish tacos, p92

Dinner 7 SmartPoints value
Bacon & cabbage pasta, p146

21 SmartPoints

THURSDAY

Breakfast

Basic muesli, p54

Lunch 8 SmartPoints value

Sesame tuna with Japanese-style salad, p80

Dinner 7 SmartPoints value

Beef & broccoli with carrot noodles, p116

21 SmartPoints

FRIDAY

Breakfast 9 SmartPoints value

Mini bagels with smoked salmon, p42

Lunch 9 SmartPoints value

Chicken & avocado wrap, p70

Dinner 5 SmartPoints value

Prawn, red lentil & cauliflower curry, p120

23 SmartPoints

LITTLE EXTRAS

Snack 5 SmartPoints value

Pea & mint dip with Melba toasts, p176

Dessert

Basic poached fruit, p204

Meal plan notes

- Use any spare SmartPoints from your daily allowance on snacks, puddings or drinks.
- Repeat your favourite days on the weekends.
- All the main meal plan recipes are ready in 35 minutes or under.

Vegetarian meal plan

Perfect for veggies, or anyone else who fancies a meat-free day.

MONDAY

Breakfast 6 SmartPoints value
Granola & Greek yogurt pots, p32

Lunch 10 SmartPoints value
Mozzarella & tomato panzanella, p60

Dinner 7 SmartPoints value
Leek 'cannelloni', p158

23 SmartPoints

TUESDAY

Breakfast 7 SmartPoints value
Bircher muesli, p50

Lunch 2 SmartPoints value
Minestrone soup, p62

Dinner 10 SmartPoints value
Wild mushroom & spinach risotto, p136

19 SmartPoints

WEDNESDAY

Breakfast 3 SmartPoints value
Ricotta & peach toast, p44

Lunch 10 SmartPoints value
Halloumi pasta salad, p98

Dinner 7 SmartPoints value
Roast vegetable & freekeh salad, p154

20 SmartPoints

THURSDAY

Breakfast 6 SmartPoints value
Granola & Greek yogurt pots, p32

Lunch 9 SmartPoints value
Courgette & feta fritters, p96

Dinner 5 SmartPoints value
Veggie meatballs & courgetti, p160

20 SmartPoints

FRIDAY

Breakfast 7 SmartPoints value
Coconut pancakes with tropical fruit, p48

Lunch 5 SmartPoints value
Mushroom & spinach soup, p90

Dinner 7 SmartPoints value
Chilli & tomato tagliatelle, p124

19 SmartPoints

LITTLE EXTRAS

Snack 5 SmartPoints value
Root veg crisps with houmous, p180

Dessert 7 SmartPoints value
Courgette cake, p194

Meal plan notes

- Use any spare SmartPoints from your daily allowance on snacks, puddings or drinks.
- Repeat your favourite days on the weekends.
- The cake will keep for up to 1 week in an airtight container.
- Amend servings to suit you.

No Count meal plan

Not counting? Here are 5 days' worth of tasty menu ideas.

MONDAY

Breakfast
Porridge with spiced apple, p46

Lunch
Baked sweet potato, p76

Dinner
Harissa salmon, p134

TUESDAY

Breakfast
Ham & egg toast (without spread), p44

Lunch
Butternut squash soup, p105

Dinner
Cottage pie with sweet potato top, p130

WEDNESDAY

Breakfast
Hash with poached egg, p38

Lunch
Butternut squash falafels, p106

Dinner
Chilli con carne, p166

THURSDAY

Breakfast
Porridge with
spiced apple, p46

Lunch
Minestrone soup,
p62

Dinner
Chicken mushroom
masala, p114

FRIDAY

Breakfast
Potato & bacon frittata,
p52

Lunch
Tuna & bean salad,
p88

Dinner
Bacon & cabbage
pasta, p146

LITTLE EXTRAS

Snack
Pea & mint dip
with Melba toasts, p176

Dessert
Cinnamon ice cream
(without apples), p192

Meal plan notes

- **Repeat your favourite days on the weekends.**
- **With No Count, you can have 2 teaspoons of healthy oil a day – olive, sunflower, safflower, rapeseed or flaxseed. You can use this in cooking or to make dressings.**

The No Count food list

You can use any of these ingredients in your No Count recipes...

BAKERY

- Calorie controlled brown bread
- Crumpets

CEREALS

- Oat bran
- Porridge oats
- Puffed wheat (no added sugar or salt)
- Wheat bran, dried
- Wheatgerm, dried
- Wholegrain wheat cereal (Shredded Wheat)

COOKING INGREDIENTS

- Garlic
- Ginger, fresh
- Herbs, fresh

CRISPS, SAVOURY SNACKS & NUTS

- Popcorn, plain (no added oil or flavours)

DAIRY & EGGS

- 0% fat natural Greek yogurt
- Cottage cheese, reduced fat, natural
- Duck egg
- Egg white
- Egg, whole
- Fat free natural fromage frais
- Fat free natural yogurt
- Fromage frais, natural
- Goose egg
- Quail egg
- Quark
- Skimmed milk
- Soya yogurt, plain
- UHT skimmed milk
- Unsweetened almond milk
- Unsweetened soya milk
- Yogurt, low fat natural

FISH, MEAT & POULTRY

- Anchovies (not in oil)
- Bacon medallions
- Beef mince, extra lean (5% fat)
- Bison fillet steak, lean
- Braising steak, lean
- Bream, red or black
- Buffalo
- Chicken breast, skinless
- Chicken drumstick, skinless
- Chicken leg, skinless
- Chicken mince
- Chicken, roast, light meat, skinless
- Clams
- Cockles
- Cod
- Coley
- Crab
- Crayfish
- Dover sole
- Fillet steak, lean
- Frogs legs
- Gammon steak
- Goat
- Grey mullet
- Grouper
- Guinea fowl
- Haddock
- Hake
- Halibut
- Ham
- Heart
- Hoki
- John Dory
- Kangaroo steak
- Kidney: lamb, pig
- King prawns
- Lemon sole
- Liver
- Lobster
- Monkfish
- Mussels
- Octopus
- Orange roughy
- Ostrich
- Oysters
- Partridge
- Pigeon
- Pike
- Plaice
- Pollock
- Pork escalope
- Pork fillet
- Pork leg joint, lean
- Pork loin steak, lean
- Pork mince, extra lean (5% fat)
- Pork shoulder joint, lean
- Pork tenderloin
- Prawns
- Quail
- Rabbit
- Rainbow trout
- Red mullet
- Red snapper (Red sea bream)
- Rock salmon (Dog fish)
- Roe
- Rump steak, lean
- Salmon
- Salmon, pink or red, canned
- Sardines, fresh

- Scallops
- Sea bass
- Sea bream
- Seafood selection
- Seafood sticks
- Shark
- Shrimps
- Silverside, lean
- Sirloin steak, lean
- Skate
- Smoked cod
- Smoked haddock
- Smoked trout
- Snails
- Sprats
- Squid
- Stewing steak, lean
- Swordfish
- Tiger prawns
- Tilapia
- Tripe
- Trout
- Tuna in brine, drained
- Tuna in spring water, drained
- Tuna, raw
- Turbot
- Turkey breast fillet
- Turkey breast mince
- Turkey breast, skinless
- Turkey rasher
- Turkey steak
- Turkey thigh
- Turkey, roast, skinless
- Turkey, wafer thin
- Veal escalope
- Venison
- Wafer thin chicken
- Whelks
- Whiting
- Wild boar
- Winkles, cooked

FRUIT & VEGETABLES

- Fresh (except avocado)
- Frozen
- Tinned in natural juice or water, drained

TINS, PACKETS & JARS

- Aduki beans
- Amaranth grain
- Baked beans
- Black eyed beans
- Borlotti beans
- Broad beans
- Brown basmati rice
- Brown rice
- Buckwheat
- Bulgar wheat
- Butter beans
- Cannellini beans
- Chick peas
- Flageolet beans
- Freekeh
- French beans
- Haricot beans
- Kidney beans
- Lentils
- Millet
- Mixed beans
- Mung beans
- Pickled beetroot
- Pickled gherkins
- Pickled onions
- Pinto beans
- Quinoa
- Soya beans
- Spelt
- Sugar free jelly crystals
- Sugar free jelly, ready to eat
- Wholewheat couscous
- Wholewheat pasta
- Wild rice
- Yellow split peas

VEGETARIAN FOODS

- Quorn fillet
- Quorn mince
- Quorn pieces
- Soya mince
- Tofu, plain
- Tofu, smoked

WEIGHT WATCHERS PRODUCTS

- Extra trimmed Unsmoked Back Bacon
- High Protein White & Wholemeal Pitta Breads
- White Wraps
- Petits Pains
- Quark
- Sliced Brown Bread
- Sliced Brown Danish Bread
- Tortilla Wraps

Use these ingredients in the quantities specified, for zero SmartPoints. If no quantity is specified, you can use as much as you like.

- **Capers, 1 tsp**
- **Chilli (fresh, dried or flakes)**
- **Fat-free tomato salsa, 1 tsp**
- **Fish sauce (Nam Pla), 1 tbsp**
- **Garlic** • **Ginger**
- **Harissa paste, °1 tsp**
- **Herbs & spices (fresh or dried)**
- **Hot pepper sauce (Tabasco), 1 tsp**
- **Lemongrass**
- **Lemon or lime juice**
- **Mustard (any), 1 tsp**
- **Soy sauce, 1 tsp**
- **Tomato purée, 1 tsp**
- **Unsweetened pickled veg, 1 tbsp**
- **Vanilla extract, 1 tsp**
- **Vinegar**
- **Worcestershire sauce, 1 tsp**
- **Yeast extract (Marmite), 1 tsp**
- **Zest of lemon, lime or orange, 1 tsp**

Recipe index

SmartPoints index